CONQUERING YOUR STRESS AND FEARS:

A treatment guide for anxiety and

Trauma-related disorders

Gustavo Kinrys, M.D., Harvard
Medical School

BOSTON
PRESS GROUP

COPYRIGHT NOTICE

This book contains the opinions and ideas of its author. It is solely for educational and informational purposes and should not be regarded as a substitute for professional medical treatment. The nature of your body's health condition is complex and unique. Therefore, you should consult a health professional before you begin any new exercise, nutrition, or supplementation program or if you have questions about your health. Neither the author nor the publisher shall be liable or responsible for any loss or damage allegedly arising from any information or suggestion in this book.

The statements in this book about food products or consumables have not been evaluated by the Food and Drug Administration (FDA). Neither the publisher nor the author are responsible for your specific health or allergy needs that may require medical supervision. Neither the publisher nor the author are responsible for any adverse reactions to the consumption of food or products that have been suggested or mentioned in this book.

If you are experiencing severe anxiety, depression, suicidal thoughts, or thoughts of harming others, it is essential for your safety and of others that you consult a psychiatrist, your primary care physician, or go to the nearest emergency room.

ISBN: 978-1-7326689-0-4

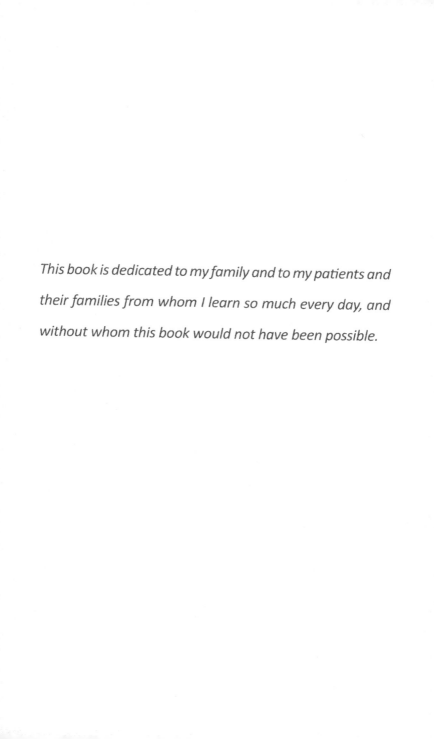

This book is dedicated to my family and to my patients and their families from whom I learn so much every day, and without whom this book would not have been possible.

TABLE OF CONTENTS

PREFACE

This book is a practical guide that focuses on managing complex psychological conditions such as fear, stress and anxiety for which conventional prescription medications may have failed to help or is undesirable since they cannot be utilized by everyone. In addition, prescription medications have a wide range of unpleasant side effects, and on occasion carry the risk of being addictive. You will find a practical and easy-to-follow approach in these pages to mitigate psychological conditions using nutrient-based remedies, herbal-based remedies, and non-pharmacological treatments.

Proper and consistent information is provided on the effective use of nutrition and herbal-based remedies to facilitate a quick and complete recovery from anxiety, stress and fear. Detailed sections are included on the most effective remedies; their origin, benefits, dosage, and in some cases, side effects.

In the case of non-pharmacological treatments, adequate information is provided on prominent complementary therapies and productive lifestyle changes such as Meditation, Cognitive Behavioral Therapy, Virtual Reality treatment, Mindfulness, Exercise, and other physical activities. All this information is compiled in this book and presented in a self-help approach to make the information easy to access and adequately utilized.

CHAPTER 1

ANXIETY, STRESS, AND FEAR

ANXIETY

Anxiety is a feeling every one of us experiences at some point in time. The 21st century we live in is fast-paced, with increasingly rapid transformation of institutions and structures. The fear of keeping up with the present times is enough to make us anxious. For some, the financial and economic challenges facing us and the thought of providing for our loved ones is worrisome. It is perfectly normal to be anxious and to worry about how to make our life worthwhile. Some individuals get anxious when it is time to speak in public – a situation known as stage fright, which is perfectly normal – for they have a fear of fumbling their words, saying or behaving inappropriately or being ridiculed. Over time, and with consistent practice in speaking in public, that anxiety diminishes.

Anxiety is quite normal, but it can become a problem in the life of the average person when the feeling is frequent and intense. Medically, such a situation is known as anxiety disorder. Like other issues we shall address in this study, the challenge starts with differentiating normal anxiety from anxiety disorder. The situation could begin with normal anxiety and later transform into a disorder. Anxiety disorder occurs when excessive worry and fear takes over an individual's life. Unnecessary paranoia usually manifests at this stage making random, but normal events breed fear in the daily life of such individuals. Anxiety could be in the form of panic attacks, phobia or even social anxiety, but to date, scientists have been unable to determine the exact moment when normal anxiety becomes anxiety disorder.

Do you worry excessively and later find out the reasons for your fear are invalid? This does not in any way indicate that you suffer from anxiety disorder, but you should certainly be cautious of these worries.

The next section discusses signs that might indicate a case of anxiety disorder.

SIGNS AND SYMPTOMS

1. **Excessive worry**

The most common symptom of anxiety is excessive worry. What is the difference between excessive worry and normal worry? In psychology, the benchmark for concluding whether or not a scenario is excessive differs from individual to individual. In terms of anxiety disorder, worrying becomes excessive when it begins to take over a person's life. You can ask yourself some questions to determine if you worry excessively. They include:

- Do you worry to the extent that it affects your concentration and productivity in school or at work?
- Do you worry to the extent that it affects the lives of your family and loved ones?
- Do you find yourself changing your lifestyle as a result of fear?
- Do your friends complain that you are becoming excessively paranoid?

If your answer to any of these four questions is yes, then you may be getting worried excessively. While spy movies can make anyone slightly more paranoid about being followed or hunted, ordinarily, it should not extend into your real life.

2. **Insomnia**

A lot of us have trouble sleeping occasionally due to some remarkable event. For some people, it's the pressure of an event such as their final examinations. For others, it could be the day before their interview for the big job they have always wanted. All these are situations where anxiety prevents people from sleeping is perfectly normal. A situation where one consistently has trouble falling asleep or staying asleep can be linked with a range of health challenges, including anxiety disorder. Note that insomnia includes waking up too early in the morning without being able to go back to bed.

Statistics from health.com indicate that half of the individuals with anxiety disorder tend to be afflicted with insomnia. The National Institute of Health estimates that approximately 30 percent of the general adult population experiences chronic insomnia in the United States. This is not surprising considering the uphill battle a lot of people encounter while going through personal and societal problems. The rule of thumb is as follows: insomnia is said to be chronic if it occurs at least three times a week. The challenge with chronic insomnia is that it is difficult to link it with anxiety disorder, but experiences have shown that they correlate.

3. **Irrational fears**

For some individuals, the fears they experience are attached to some particular objects, situations or events. They may have lived with those fears throughout their lifetime and may not know there is a problem till they are faced with scenarios that unearth such fears in them. People even have phobias about seemingly insignificant things, but an understanding and acceptance of the fact that they face such a fear is the first step in managing it.

For instance, someone may have a fear of reptiles but it would never manifest because they have never had any encounter with such creatures. Then a planned excursion to the zoo would suddenly bring out such fears in full force when they see one. Phobias can be disruptive and challenging in cases where the individual encounters such phobias consistently. Individuals with Agoraphobia (fear of crowds) may be involved in situations where they have to face a large crowd often. In such instances, the phobia would most likely affect their productivity and effectiveness.

In some cases of irrational fear, the fact that an individual can avoid such situations may be enough to keep the problem at bay. But in instances where there is no other option and the individual has to frequently face the situation that evokes the fear, working to overcome the fear is vital.

4. **Self-consciousness**

Everyone should be self-conscious. We need to watch how we talk, move or eat. Typical standards of etiquette are society's way of making sure we blend in to live and relate to each other as normal individuals. For some people, excessive awareness of themselves and their situation could be a great challenge. People with social anxiety disorder usually feel everyone is watching or judging their every action or lack of action. They usually worry about not meeting people's standards of them and this makes it very difficult for them to relate normally to other members of society. This challenge is exhibited in certain mannerisms, excessive sweating, talking difficulties, trembling and nausea.

5. **Reliving painful memories**

Life is full of ups and downs. A lot of us have faced one traumatic event or the other. Some people never get over these events and may continually be triggered by situations or objects in their daily lives which force them to relieve those traumatic memories over and again. For instance, individuals with post-traumatic stress disorder suddenly and consistently experience flashbacks to violent situations. This is common amongst war veterans and police officers. Some may even try to avoid places and individuals that remind them of such experiences, but when they can't and they are faced with such a situation, they tend to lose control.

6. **Panic attacks**

A panic attack is an event characterized by the sudden surge of intense fear and discomfort which escalates within a short period of time. The fear experienced within this short period of time is usually disproportionate to the situation the individual is actually facing. Panic attacks are usually very brief and the whole episode sometimes takes less than ten minutes. According to the National Institute of Mental Health (NIMH) and the Anxiety and depression Association of America (ADAA), panic disorders are quite common in the United States, affecting about 6 million individuals. Also, females are more likely to experience these attacks than males. An individual that has experienced a panic attack once is very likely to experience it again. The symptoms of panic attacks include:

- Accelerated heart rate

- Discomfort

- Trembling

- Tingling sensations

- Abdominal pain

- Heat sensation

- Fainting

7. **Compulsive disorders**

It is good to have routines and guidelines on how to do things. Almost everyone has certain actions they perform daily. For example, I like taking tea every morning before starting my day. I also watch the 6 a.m. news as part of my daily routine. For some people, it could be cleaning their house every morning or jogging for thirty minutes every evening after work.

To determine whether your routine is considered obsessive, ask yourself how you feel when that particular sequence is terminated. Do you suddenly become unbalanced on a day when you are unable to jog in the evening? Do you find yourself losing your cool because you could not watch your favorite TV program at the stated time? Does the fact that you could not carry out your favorite activity push you into panic mode? If the answer to any of these questions is yes, you may be experiencing obsessive-compulsive disorder. People with this condition tend to have a strict, structured way of carrying out most of their activities, including the minor ones. Whenever they are disturbed from these activities, it sets off a serious chain reaction.

In conclusion, anxiety and anxiety disorders are two different concepts. While the former is perfectly normal, the latter is not. Anxiety disorders are one of the focus points of this book and subsequent chapters will discuss natural therapies that can ameliorate the challenge.

STRESS

After a hard day's work or after experiencing tough situations, a lot of people claim they are stressed. Most times, the situation they are referring to is a straightforward case of fatigue. Stress is much more than fatigue.

Stress is our body's method of reacting to the demands we face. Being stressed is quite normal for any hardworking, productive individual, with a little dose of stress sometimes being positive for the person. It could be a source of motivation or inspiration to getting the job done, and may be a source of pride that all our efforts and exertions led to something productive. Imagine all the stress you went through while in school till graduation, but remember also how fulfilled you were afterwards.

What helped you through that tough scenario is known as stress response. Stress is vital to the body's metabolism and can even save you from dangerous situations by helping with the stimulation of chemicals that alert you to the dangers ahead. The chemicals are stimulated when the nervous system sends hormones like adrenaline to prepare the body for emergency situations. The heart rate increases, blood pressure rises and sensory organs become sharper than normal. You find yourself facing danger squarely or running away from it thanks to your stress receptors.

The downside to this response is that your body produces the same response whether you are facing emotional stress or physical stress. This usually leads to chronic stress which, when left unmanaged, may cause serious havoc. It could be so damaging as to affect all vital systems of the body. The damages it can cause include:

- Insomnia

- Depression

- Constipation

- Loneliness

- Flu

- Anger

- Poor judgment

- Constant worrying

- Body pains

- Loss of sex drive

- Memory problems

- Heart diseases

- Autoimmune diseases, etc.

The causes of chronic stress vary from individual to individual. What may lead to stress in your life may be perfectly managed by another individual. There is no rule of thumb on what would cause stress in an individual's life. Several general causes of stress have been identified, including problems at school or work, marital challenges, financial difficulty, challenges adapting to new situations, and other major life changes.

The most important step in learning to control and manage chronic stress is identifying the underlying causes of the stress you are facing. It is quite common for individuals who are stressed to seek isolation; but that hardly helps. As will be reiterated several times in this study, no man is an island, and every form of therapy we recommend requires having a strong support system to help you complete the journey.

You may consider stress a minor thing which you experience and cope with easily, but the reality is there are lots of people who are not as fortunate. They reside in your community (about 40 percent of Americans claim they have faced stress issues at one point in their lives), and it is your role to help them overcome the obstacles they are going to face along the journey to recovery. Chronic stress clearly kills the quality of life of the average individual if it is left unattended. It affects the ability to concentrate on basic tasks and consequently, people find themselves making more mistakes than usual. The hormone released due to chronic stress, i.e. cortisol, channels glucose to the muscles during the stress response and this affects brain cell communication.

The American Psychological Association (APA) asserts that chronic stress can hamper an individual's ability to recover from heart attacks. Stress response sometimes turns off blood flow to the skin which, if consistent, may cause quick aging. This explains why individuals who are stressed usually look older than they truly are.

Chronic stress is certainly a situation that should be avoided at all costs by every individual.

You can ask yourself some questions to determine if you are experiencing chronic stress. These questions include:

- Do you find yourself in deep thought to the extent of losing awareness?

- Do you often forget basic events and objects like car keys?

- Do you often find yourself afraid?

- Do you find people complaining about a change in your behavior?

While the above are not the only signals that indicate chronic stress, they are things you should take into cognizance.

FACTORS THAT AFFECT YOUR STRESS LEVEL

1. **How you deal with emotions and events**

   Whenever you experience shocking situations, how do you handle it? It is normal to be ruffled when the unexpected happens, but our response, to a large extent, determines whether it weighs us down for long. Do little tantrums and actions of other people get to you? Are you easily offended by the pettiness of others? If you are the type of individual that feels hurt easily, chronic stress may easily affect you. Whenever you are angry, do you calm yourself down easily, or do you let that anger grow? All these are pertinent questions you need to provide answers to.

2. **Your support network**

   Do you have individuals you can easily talk to when you feel down? Do you trust your family and friends enough to share your burdens with them? It is often said that a problem shared is half solved. If you are an individual who has no one to turn to for help whenever challenges arise, you are more likely to feel overwhelmed and alone; this provides the perfect platform for stress to build up in your system. While at times being alone is wise, especially for self-reflection and assessment of our actions, it is not a way of life to be totally embraced.

3. **Your level of preparedness**

How ready are you for the worst? Are you someone who thinks three steps ahead? Or do you live one day at a time? While none of these lifestyles should be frowned at, balance is the key. You should not be caught unaware by any situation. You should have a plan in case the worst happens. For instance, if you take a job expecting rigorous working hours and an intense cut-throat environment, you certainly would be more prepared if it happens than someone who came in with no expectations.

4. **How well you believe in yourself**

You are obviously not Superman, and even if you were, Clark Kent has weaknesses. Obviously, you are not infallible or indomitable, but how well do you trust your own abilities? No one can trust or believe in you more than your humble self. Coming to this self-realization would provide you with the necessary boost to help work through a lot of the obstacles that may come your way.

5. **Your philosophy of life**

Are you a glass half-full or a glass half-empty individual? This metaphor simply seeks to help you realize how optimistic or pessimistic you may be about the situations of life. When you believe things are going to get worse rather than better, you are indirectly assuring your brain that you cannot find a way past the obstacles facing you. This causes stress reactors to overwork, which in turn leads to chronic stress.

FEAR

Fear is a response in the brain that begins with a stressful stimulus and ends with the arrival of chemicals that cause a racing heart, fast breathing and invigorated muscles in addition to other things. This is also known as the fight-or-flight response. The stimulus could be a spider or other type of bug, a knife blade at your throat, a gun pointed at you, a theater loaded to the brim with people sitting tight waiting for you to give a talk, or the sudden crash of your front door against the door frame as if someone is breaking into.

The brain is a significantly complex organ. It is composed of more than 100 billion nerve cells involved in a complex system of communication that processes all we sense, think and do. Some of these communications prompt conscious ideas and action, while others produce autonomic responses. The fear response is altogether autonomic: We

24

don't deliberately trigger it or even recognize what's happening until it gets to the point where it has run its course.

Since cells in the brain are continually exchanging data and activating responses, many areas of the brain can get peripherally engaged with fear. Research has found that specific parts of the brain play a vital role in the fear response, including:

- Thalamus: determines where incoming sensory information should be sent (from eyes, ears, mouth, and skin).

- Sensory cortex: translates sensory information.

- Hippocampus: stores and recovers conscious memories; forms sets of stimuli to create context.

- Amygdala: deciphers feelings and emotions; arbitrates conceivable threats; stores fear memories.

- Hypothalamus: enacts "fight or flight" response.

The process of creating fear starts with a terrifying stimulus and ends with the fight-or-flight response. Fear is an inclination instigated by a perceived threat or danger that might happen in any person, which causes a change in metabolic and organ capacities and eventually an adjustment in behavior such as fleeing, stowing away, or being frozen in place.

The fear an individual feels might be based on a past experience that is casting light on a stimulus happening in the present, or it might be based on a suspicion of a future danger perceived to be hazardous to the body or life itself. The fear response emerges from the perception of danger, prompting a showdown or escape from the danger, or maintaining a strategic distance from it (otherwise called the fight-or-flight response), which in outrageous instances of

26

fear (frightfulness and dread) can invoke the freeze response, or paralysis.

Fear is adjusted through the procedure of cognition and learning. In this way, fear is arbitrated as logical and appropriate, or illogical and inappropriate. An illogical fear is known as a phobia. Specialists propose there are just a handful of essential or intrinsic feelings and that fear is one of them. Others include acute stress response, anger, apprehension, anxiety, dread, horror, happiness, panic, and pity. Fear is firmly identified with anxiety and occurs as an after-effect of a danger seen as wild or unavoidable. The fear response serves survival by creating proper behavioral responses, which is why it has been safeguarded all through evolution.

SIGNS AND SYMPTOMS

Numerous physiological changes in the body are related to fear. An inherent response for adapting to danger, fear works by quickening the breathing rate (hyperventilation) and the heart rate. It narrows the fringe blood vessels prompting blushing and vasodilation of the focal vessels (pooling), expands muscle tension including the muscles connected to every hair follicle causing them to contract which produces "the shivers" -- clinically known as piloerection. Fear also causes sweating, elevated blood glucose (hyperglycemia), elevated serum calcium, increment in white blood cells called neutrophilic leukocytes, alertness prompting sleep disturbance and "butterflies in the belly".

CAUSES

Individuals create particular fears because of learning. This has been contemplated in brain science as fear conditioning, starting with John B. Watson's Little Albert experiment in 1920 which was inspired in the wake of watching a child with an illogical fear of dogs. In this research, an 11-month-old boy was adapted to fear a white rat in the laboratory. The fear became noticeably generalized to include other white, furry items like a dog, a rabbit, and even a bundle of cotton.

Fear can be learned by encountering or watching an alarming, horrendous mishap. For instance, if a child falls into a well and battles to get out, he or she may build up a fear of wells, heights (acrophobia), enclosed spaces (claustrophobia), or water (aqua phobia). There are studies that take a gander at ranges of the brain influenced by fear. When examining these ranges (for example, the amygdala), it was suggested that humans experience fear not only when they themselves encounter trauma, but also when they see fear in others. In one particular research study, the amygdala of subjects were influenced when watching another person being submitted to an aversive occasion realizing they, themselves, awaited the same experience, and also when they were placed in a fear-inciting circumstance.

Fear is influenced by social and historical settings. For instance, in the mid-twentieth century, numerous Americans feared polio, an infection that can prompt loss of motion (paralysis). There are multifaceted contrasts in how individuals react to fear. Display rules influence how likely individuals are to demonstrate the outward appearance of fear and different feelings. While many fears are learned, the ability to fear is a fundamental human instinct. Many researchers have discovered that specific fears (e.g. heights, animals) are significantly more typical than others (e.g. mists, clouds, flowers). Additionally, these fears are simpler to initiate. This concept is known as readiness. Since early humans feared perilous circumstances, yet survived and procreated, readiness is hypothesized to be a hereditary impact. From the viewpoint of evolutionary psychology, diverse fears might be distinctive adjustments that have been valuable in our evolutionary past. They may have been created amid various eras. A few fears, such as the fear of heights, might be normal to all well-evolved mammals and created amid the Mesozoic time frame. Different fears, the fear of snakes for instance, might be normal to all simians and created amid the Cenozoic day and age. All things considered, other fears such as the fear of rats or bugs might be one of a kind to humans and created amid the Paleolithic and Neolithic eras (when rats and creepy crawlies wound up as bearers of contagious ailments and proved destructive for crops and stored foods).

CHAPTER 2

NUTRITIENT-BASED REMEDIES

During recent years the consumption of nutrient-based remedies as a type of treatment for different afflictions has become progressively better known in Western societies. Nutrient-based remedies have been broadly utilized and, for the most part, acknowledged as established treatments for stress, anxiety, and related disorders.

Although regular medication is accessible and extremely effective, the side effects in some cases are more awful than the anxiety itself. In the event that you are experiencing some type of stress or anxiety and might want to treat the symptoms with dietary supplements, it is recommended that you attempt a portion of the wholesome supplements that will be talked about in consequent pages (as it relates to the conditions you are experiencing). They are safe, effective, and powerful, and if utilized appropriately, can work to help facilitate a quick recovery from anxiety, stress and fear.

INOSITOL

Inositol is a pseudo-vitamin and is erroneously said to be a B-vitamin (Vitamin B8) normally found in plants and animals. Inositol is regularly known as myo-inositol because of its dynamic stereoisomer. It has a chemical structure similar to glucose.

Inositol is a starch and it tastes sweet, yet it is not as sweet as normal sugar (sucrose). Inositol is the word used in dietary supplements while myo-inositol is the favored name. Additionally, inositol is a critical part of basic lipids and its different phosphates (phospholipids).

The essential function of inositol is to keep fats from gathering in the body, especially in the liver. Inositol is included into caffeinated drinks since it is useful in converting nutrients into energy. The highest levels of inositol concentration are found in the heart; it works with neurotransmitters in message circulation.

One of the major reasons people do not get enough sleep at night is over-thinking. The human brain can't sleep and thoughts continue to travel back and forth, thereby keeping you awake. The thought process is guided by serotonin, a hormone. At the point when serotonin levels are low, you can't sleep; so keeping up ideal levels of serotonin promotes profound and sound sleep. Inositol works extremely well with serotonin and ensures that the levels are sufficiently high to influence you to feel peaceful during your sleeping hours.

Inositol promotes healthy serotonin levels as well as communicates with the GABA receptors in the brain. GABA receptors' proper function guarantees that you keep your cool. In circumstances of higher stress, GABA receptors don't work accurately, thereby causing insomnia. Inositol keeps a tab on the best possible workings of GABA receptors and ensures that they are ready to give you anxiety-free and stress-free tranquility. Inositol works truly well here as it nearly impersonates the functions of drained GABA receptors and fills in as a substitute. When you're having a sleepless night, supplementing with inositol can be a smart idea. Inositol needs to develop in your system, so administering an everyday dosage of 0.5 grams to 2 grams for a month ought to stimulate serene sleep. Inositol in a single dose daily won't be powerful, so if you are having countless sleepless nights, you can take inositol two hours before you go to bed for at least one month.

It is believed that inositol is one of the best nutrient-based remedies for anxiety and it doesn't have many if any side effects. Inositol consumption brings down anxiety symptoms. GABA receptors are in charge of keeping you cool and drained levels of these make you anxious. It replaces the non-useful GABA receptors and takes on a similar role. Individuals experiencing anxiety, more often than not, have low levels of serotonin. Administration of inositol helps in controlling serotonin levels, consequently granting a calm mindset. The dosage is by all accounts high, however, inositol is normally found in the body and side effects like gastric inconvenience or loose stools are very rare.

Obsessive Compulsive Disorder (OCD) is a physiological disorder conceivably caused because of lower levels of serotonin. So once more, inositol becomes an integral factor. Inositol is converted into two neurotransmitter chemicals in the brain that control serotonin levels. A research study carried out on different OCD patients discovered that supplementing with inositol slowly improves OCD and causes depression levels to improve. Inositol is commonly combined with choline, which is a natural medication for the treatment of OCD as well. Choline is found in almost all animal tissues and is necessary for normal synaptic transmission. Inositol is included as a synergist and assists choline in the liver metabolism of cholesterol and other lipids.

Combined choline and inositol is a recommended supplement and should be utilized under the care of a qualified doctor. Individuals experiencing OCD must never ingest caffeine, as caffeine expands the brain activities and causes reductions in inositol levels. There is no established or Reference Dietary Intake (RDI) dosage for OCD patients. It is recommended that OCD patients see a doctor for the required dosage.

The benefits of inositol supplements include:

- Fighting the symptoms of depression

- Utilization as part of cancer treatment (inositol hexaphosphate)

- Enhancing weight loss

- Liver detoxification (when used with choline)

- Enhancement of blood circulation

Pregnant women and breast-feeding moms are not encouraged to take inositol; however, there is no indication that it produces side effects. Nausea is a typical response related to B-vitamin ingestion, and can be settled by administrating smaller doses at first to accustom the body to it. Aside from this, if inositol is blended with different substances it may have side effects. However, it ought to be a safe supplement to ingest since the body usually disposes of excess amounts straightaway.

LYSINE

For quite some time it has been postulated that the dysregulation of neurotransmitters might be a reason for anxiety. These neurotransmitters include GABA, serotonin, dopamine and norepinephrine. Amino acids, for example, L-tyrosine and L-tryptophan are known forerunners for particular neurotransmitters. Recent studies in animals have distinguished two other amino acids, L-lysine and L-arginine, which may impact neurotransmitters associated with stress and anxiety. L-lysine has appeared to go about as a fractional serotonin receptor 4 (5-HT4) rival, diminishing the brain-gut response to stress and in addition, diminishing blood cortisol levels.

The fortification of lysine and olive leaf herb extracts diminishes anxiety and reduces stress levels. Individuals who experience the ill effects of depression regularly have low L-lysine levels. Lysine supplementation is prescribed to them to help with the symptoms. It comes in both oral packages and as a cream for topical application to treat distinctive heath disorders.

L-Lysine supplements are broadly used to treat anxiety, stress, insomnia and mood disorders. Lysine helps the human body in the following ways:

- It is a forerunner to L-carnitine. It causes you to shed off excess fat and upgrades the memory and concentration

- It is a magnificent immune booster

- It protects the human body against coronary illness

- It helps the generation of human development hormone

- It controls outbreaks of herpes

Lysine is an essential component of the human. It is viewed as safe and non-poisonous. Dissimilar to other anti-anxiety medications, it comes with no side effects. It is readily available in an assortment of food products; however, due to improper dietary arrangement or flawed dietary patterns, the body can have an insufficiency of Lysine. So, to address the lack, Lysine supplements are given to the patients.

Now and again, Lysine is joined with Arginine to standardize typical stress responses in patients with traits of high anxiety levels. The treatment also has demonstrated viability to standardize basal cortisol levels in humans. Most basic anxiety disorders that are dealt with by lysine supplementation are:

- Panic Disorder

- Obsessive Compulsive Disorder

- Post-traumatic stress disorder (PTSD)

- Generalized Anxiety Disorder (GAD)

- Social Anxiety disorder (SAD)

Lysine deficiency is most usually experienced in veggie lovers or individuals with insignificant animal products in their diet and nutritional regimen. This can create symptoms of anxiety. In any case, the fortunate thing about L-Lysine supplements is that they are easily accessible. You can shed the fear of a panic attack and look for help with your body's capacity to adapt to stress by taking these supplements.

With so diverse nutrient-based remedies for anxiety available over the counter, you need not experience the ill effects of symptoms. Seek the counsel of your family doctor or psychiatrist today to discover the viability of this supplement for your concerns.

L-TYROSINE

Tyrosine is a powerful, sweet-smelling amino acid that is a building block for dopamine, epinephrine, norepinephrine, and thyroid hormones. Tyrosine supplements are nootropics and adaptogens that assist with performance amid times of stress. It helps fundamentally with fatigue from stress. It is found in some high-protein food, such as, meat, cheese, fish, dairy products, beans, nuts, and oats. Some nutrient-based supplements additionally utilize this amino acid as an ingredient.

In the body, tyrosine is predominantly utilized in the brain as a forerunner to a class of neurotransmitters called catecholamines (dopamine, norepinephrine, and epinephrine). These catecholamines are utilized as part of various cognitive capacities. To end up noticeably a catecholamine, tyrosine requires two transformative advances. To start with, it must be converted into dihydroxyphenylalanine (DOPA). At that point, an enzyme (generally some type of a decarboxylase) transforms the DOPA into one of the three catecholamines.

Many studies have been done on its effects. Findings show that L-Tyrosine appears to reduce stress, enhance memory, and improve discernment. Some people take it to boost mental sharpness and sleep better during the night. There are many other minor, though recognizable, advantages to consuming L-Tyrosine supplements. And as you may expect, it can be extremely useful for overseeing anxiety symptoms.

A lot of users have expressed that L-Tyrosine supplementation worked when other normal solutions didn't. They reported their anxiety attacks were less successive and serious, and they felt their anxiety was reduced in social situations. It can likewise help in normalizing appetite and sleeping patterns. While it's very uncommon for individuals to be inadequate in L-Tyrosine since it is created in the body, you can supplement with extra L-Tyrosine to benefit from its calming affects. Many individuals have encountered a discernible decrease in anxiety after including a greater amount of this amino acid in their diet. Be that as it may, why precisely does this happen?

To put it succinctly, L-Tyrosine enhances dopamine creation due to its part as a building block. Dopamine is a neurotransmitter that controls feelings of pleasure as well as memory, state of mind, attention, and sleep. At the point when there is an inadequacy of dopamine, it can prompt symptoms like anxiety and depression.

Since L-Tyrosine appears to build dopamine levels, it might be a critical advantage for individuals who are feeling more on edge than ordinary. It doesn't work for everybody, even though individuals with anxiety have reported diminished symptoms and can manage better for the duration of the day. Some of the advantages include; elevated mood, better mental clearness, and higher energy levels. Scientists view the benefits as extremely encouraging, and it is one of the more solid alternatives.

Also, we can't overlook that L-Tyrosine's dopamine bolster has general advantages for memory, focus, and more. This amino acid can have recognizable advantages for both your temperament and mental execution, which is the reason such a significant number of people are taking it. In case you're searching for a natural product with these advantages, L-Tyrosine supplementation is hard to beat.

In any case, remember that supplements should never be a substitution for genuine pharmaceutical or mental health care. If you are encountering extreme anxiety that is influencing your personal satisfaction with life, it is best to see a specialist before using any medication. Individuals may react adversely to the ingredients in supplements, so you generally need to limit the danger of side effects.

Additionally, there is a vast difference in L-Tyrosine dosage. Some individuals think it's effective at just 200mg a day, while others may need substantially more than that to have a noticeable impact. It is suggested that you converse with your specialist for help in finding the best viable dosage for your body.

MAGNESIUM

Magnesium is a positively charged ion, a cation that is engaged with numerous imperative molecular functions in the body and has been linked with fighting off anxiety symptoms and anxiety-related disorders. Magnesium is a calming mineral that has been found to initiate relaxation. As indicated by the University of Maryland Medical Center, deficiency in magnesium diminishes levels of the neurotransmitter serotonin, and antidepressants have appeared to build magnesium in the brain which is proof of a positive connection. Magnesium can act at the blood brain barrier to prevent the passage of stress hormones into the brain.

Magnesium is a factor in over 300 chemical responses in the body, and research demonstrates that magnesium insufficiency adds to various mental and emotional symptoms including stress, insomnia and anxiety. Furthermore, magnesium plays a part in adjusting calcium levels in the body. A lot of people know about the way calcium and bone health go hand-in-hand, but a lesser known fact is that without magnesium, calcium levels are persistently imbalanced. In instances of serious magnesium inadequacy, calcium may even toxically affect the brain.

There have been a few studies on how stress impacts the level of magnesium found in the body. Such research shows that during high stress periods, magnesium is used at a significantly more rapid rate than during normal periods and can be quickly drained. At the point when the magnesium stored is completely spent, unless it is replaced, long term anxiety is frequently the outcome. This anxiety might be treated with multiple medications and yet this does nothing to remedy the basic issue.

Magnesium is likewise fundamental for GABA movement; it improves GABA sensitivity on nerve receptors, yet this is only one of the numerous basic functions of magnesium in the body. Magnesium is incredible as a muscle relaxant, and additionally has a calming impact, and it's one of the numerous minerals that is, for the most part, inadequate in our modern diet, which explains the high levels of anxiety we see today. Low levels of magnesium are related to an entire scope of disorders including diabetes, high blood pressure, and thyroid imbalances in addition to anxiety, so a magnesium supplement comes highly recommended for people with any of these conditions.

Magnesium is probably not going to be a lasting remedy for every individual who experiences anxiety or insomnia, yet it is very powerful in lessening or totally taking out stress, anxiety and sleeplessness in the individuals who are even marginally lacking. Be that as it may, all consumers should address a doctor or other authorized human services professional before rolling out any dietary improvements.

GABA

The vast majority of the substances used to ease anxiety, including alcohol, cannabis and sedatives, get their impact by boosting GABA in the brain. So could GABA itself be a valuable supplement to stop anxiety? Gamma-aminobutyric acid (GABA) occurs normally in your brain where it works as a neurotransmitter and manages brain movement. It is additionally required in different parts of your body, where its most essential function is managing muscle tone.

Not at all like other neurotransmitters, GABA has an inhibitory capacity: it has a tendency to slow down neuron firing. Different neurotransmitters; adrenaline, nor-adrenaline, serotonin, dopamine, glutamate have an excitatory capacity, i.e. they fortify neuron firing. It's vital to recall this distinction when you are going to choose the best supplement to take for anxiety or depression.

Without enough GABA, neurons fire effortlessly over and over again. The moment it becomes too excessive, you can't get moving. GABA is, in fact, an amino acid. However, it's not part of any protein either in the nourishment you eat, or in your body. You can get it in little sums from food, yet in large part, it is orchestrated in your body from glutamate: something you in all likelihood have a lot of.

A large number of the prescriptions and remedies for anxiety utilized today influence the levels of GABA and how it functions in your brain. Benzodiazepines (medications, for example, Xanax and Valium) reduce anxiety through the way they cooperate with the GABA receptors. (Then again, coffee represses GABA, and so can make you more on edge or hummed up). While GABA tends to upgrade serotonin in your brain (generally something worth being thankful for), it also has a tendency to decrease some different neurotransmitters (adrenaline, nor-adrenaline, dopamine). That is useful if the levels are too high (as is likely with anxiety), yet not in the event that you are depressed!

Regardless of whether you choose to attempt a GABA supplement or not, you have to improve the way GABA works in your brain. One approach to do this is by taking additional Vitamin B6, which is required for GABA combination. Numerous GABA supplements include B6; if the GABA supplement you are taking does not, ensure you take a different B6 supplement.

Many individuals find that a GABA supplement is the ideal solution for anxiety and stress as they cite feelings of calm and serenity. Some actually find it to be excessively steadying at the doses required, making it impossible to be viable, and others again report definitely no impact from a GABA supplement. Just as is the case with other medications, it doesn't work for everybody.

5-HTP

5-hydroxytryptophan (5-HTP) is a chemical that the body makes from tryptophan (a fundamental amino acid that you get from food). After tryptophan is changed into 5-HTP, the compound is changed into another substance called serotonin. 5-HTP dietary supplements help bring serotonin levels up in the brain, enhancing psychological well-being as well as the immune system. Since serotonin manages mood and behavior, 5-HTP may positively affect sleep, anxiety, craving, temperament, and pain sensation. 5-HTP isn't found in the food we eat, despite the fact that tryptophan is found in foods. Eating food with tryptophan does not build 5-HTP levels in particular, in any case. As a supplement, 5-HTP is separated from the seeds of an African plant called Griffonia simplicifolia.

5-HTP has been utilized for an assortment of conditions including anxiety, different sleep disorders, depression, hyperactivity disorders, essential fibromyalgia syndrome, cerebellar ataxia, and headaches. In young adults who experience stress and anxiety as a result of a relationship break up, a 6-week supplementation of 5-HTP can diminish anxiety in three weeks by expanding serum brain-inferred neurotrophic factor levels and serotonin levels. Given the way that 5-HTP is a building block or forerunner of the mood-upgrading compound serotonin, researchers have investigated the potential advantage of 5-HTP in bringing down anxiety. Individuals who experience the ill effects of chronic panic attacks because of lower accessibility of serotonin in the brain frequently find relief through supplementation of 200mg of 5-hydroxytryptophan. In human clinical trials, home grown concentrates of 5-HTP appeared to build GABA receptor agonists or increment GABA levels totally, advancing a feeling of relaxation and diminished anxiety.

The advantage of ingesting 5-HTP alone for sleep treatment stays indistinct. In any case, some studies demonstrate that the consumption of 5-HTP blended with GABA altogether enhances sleep quality: individuals nod off speedier as well as sleep all the more serenely. More research is expected to discover precisely how advantageous taking 5-HTP independently may be to enable falling and/or staying serenely asleep.

The Common Side Effects of 5-HTP supplements include:

- Stomach uneasiness or pain

- Looseness of the bowels

- Queasiness (Vomiting)

- Reduction in or absence of hunger

- Acid reflux, Gas or Bloating

Note that long-term supplementation with 5-HTP can Deplete Dopamine, Norepinephrine, and Epinephrine.

NUTRIENT-BASED REMEDIES

Table 1: Summary of Nutrient-Based Remedies

Nutritional Remedies	Treatments	Mechanism
Inositol	Stress, Anxiety, Insomnia and Obsessive Compulsive Disorder (OCD)	Promotes healthy serotonin levels as well as communicates with the GABA receptors in the brain.
Lysine	Panic Disorder, Obsessive Compulsive Disorder (OCD), Post-traumatic stress disorder (PTSD), Generalized Anxiety Disorder (GAD),Social Anxiety disorder (SAD)	Impacts neurotransmitters associated with stress and anxiety. Acts as a fractional serotonin receptor 4 (5-HT4) rivals, diminishing the brain-gut response to stress and in addition, diminishing blood cortisol levels.
L-Tyrosine	Depression, Anxiety, and Stress	Predominantly utilized in the brain as a forerunner to a class of neurotransmitters called catecholamines, which are used as part of various cognitive capacities.
Magnesium	Stress, insomnia and Anxiety	Acts at the blood brain barrier to prevent the passage of stress hormones into the brain. . Adjusts calcium levels in the body
GABA	Stress and Anxiety	It works as a neurotransmitter and manages brain movement. Equipped with inhibitory capacity: it has a tendency to slow down neuron firing.
5HTP	Different sleep disorders, Anxiety, Craving, and Pain Sensation, Hyperactivity disorders, Depression, Cerebellar ataxia, Essential Fibromyalgia Syndrome	Helps bring serotonin levels up in the brain, enhancing psychological well-being and the immune system.

CHAPTER 3

HERBAL-BASED REMEDIES

Consistently, a huge number of prescriptions are given out for stress and anti-anxiety medications, making them probably the most commonly recommended medications. In any case, these prescriptions don't always work and can't be utilized by everybody. In addition, these medications have a huge number of side effects.

For reasons like these, more individuals are switching to herbal-based solutions to control their stress and anxiety levels with a noticeable resurgence in the utilization of herbs. This phenomenon has been energized by the increasing expenses of prescription medications and the awareness that anti-anxiety medications like Xanax and Ativan possess serious side effects, including being probably the most addictive substances known. Natural, herbal-based remedies have long histories of safe and successful utilization, and science has demonstrated that a huge number of them work as well as stress and anti-anxiety medications.

With this perspective, I will share with you the common and most effective ones, how each one works, the symptoms they treat best, and substantially more.

CHAMOMILE

Derived from the Asteraceae group of plants, the flowers of this plant can be dried and utilized for various natural remedies and poultices. Its most prevalent form is tea. One of the mainstream teas in the marketplace, chamomile has numerous health advantages and uses. These include its capacity to guard the skin, bring down stress levels, control sleep and relieve menstrual side effects. It additionally supports the immune system, treats gastrointestinal issues, and oversees diabetes, among other things.

This plant comes in many forms, so chamomile tea from one region of the world may not be precisely the same as elsewhere. However, the vital part of the plants is very comparable and may give similar benefits. Studies have discovered that German and Roman assortments of chamomile have the tendency to contain the most grounded concentrations of advantageous compounds and supplements to individuals who drink this tea regularly.

Aside from the charming taste and accessibility of chamomile tea, it has been applauded throughout the years for its healthy advantages. The presence of flavonoids, sesquiterpenes, and other potent antioxidants in this tea effectively affect the body. While it is generally taken as a drink, the fluid can likewise be topically applied in specific cases for alleviation from different skin issues. The vast majority of the general population have profited incredibly from chamomile tea, so let's see some of its advantages and uses.

- **Alleviates Stress and anxiety:** One of the most mainstream uses of chamomile tea is to treat stress and anxiety. Following a draining day at work, the warm, calming nature of this refreshment can significantly raise the levels of serotonin and melatonin in your body. These levels can effectively wipe out stress and worry, while additionally slowing down your mind and killing common symptoms of anxiety. A cup or more of chamomile tea daily can critically help with chronic stress.

- **Actuates Sleep:** Just as chamomile tea can ease stress and tension, it can likewise be a general tranquilizer, especially for individuals who battle with restlessness, non-soothing or non-rejuvenating sleep. Indeed, even those battling with sleep apnea and different disorders may profit from the impacts of chamomile tea. Drinking a warm, non-juiced cup of chamomile tea can enable you to nod off quickly and wake up feeling more invigorated.

- **Boosts the Immune System:** If you need to reinforce your immune system to avoid diseases, chamomile tea is the appropriate response. There is a good measure of phenolic compound in chamomile tea that is particularly associated with battling bacterial contaminations in the body. Studies have demonstrated that 5-6 glasses of this tea over a course of two weeks can fundamentally enhance the body's capacity to battle diseases.

- **Eases Menstrual Discomfort:** The anti-inflammatory quality of chamomile tea makes this relaxant a mainstream option for ladies experiencing side effects from the monthly cycle such as, swelling, sweating, cramping, anxiety, inability to sleep, and emotional episodes. Chamomile tea can specifically influence a large number of these symptoms by relieving the psyche and body, and decreasing irritation that might cause inconveniences.

- **Skin and Hair Care**: Due to the calming and antioxidant rich nature of chamomile tea, it isn't solely utilized as a refreshment. Warm or icy chamomile tea can topically be applied to the site of aggravations or skin conditions, for example, dermatitis. Research demonstrates that this kind of direct application can fundamentally enhance recuperation and decrease the presence of flaws and wrinkles on the face. Eradicating oxidative stress and boosting the immune response in these regions can do wonders for your skin. Aside from the majority of the amazing characteristics of chamomile tea, numerous users assert that it enhances the appearance and quality of the hair. While the anti-inflammatory elements can reduce disturbance on the scalp, the more grounded chemicals can brace the strands of your hair, eradicate dandruff, and give your hair a superior, silky look.

- **Oversees Diabetes**: Research has demonstrated that chamomile tea can be helpful to individuals experiencing diabetes. By bringing down blood sugar levels and managing the quantity of insulin in the blood, the intense natural chemicals in chamomile help to stop gigantic drops and spikes in blood sugar.

- **Treats Stomach Issues**: If you are experiencing stomach disturbance, stretching anywhere from slight swelling to IBS symptoms, chamomile tea can be helpful in offering assistance. It has calming properties that assist to facilitate the turning nature of your gut and permit the entry of gas and smoother bowel developments. A single cup of chamomile tea can improve how you feel; however, persistent utilization of this can keep conditions from developing in your gut.

- **Treats Allergic Responses**: While chamomile is an allergen to some people, especially individuals who are sensitive to ragweed, daisies or chrysanthemum, it can tweak the immune response to allergens in the body. By functioning as an anti-histamine, chamomile tea can alleviate these unfavorably susceptible responses all through the body, thus preventing the symptoms before they become noticeable.

Drinking chamomile tea is a powerful approach to ease stress and digestive issues, anxiety, and loss of sleep to include insomnia. Natural supplements for anxiety haven't been logically tried to a pronounced degree, and this can likewise be said of chamomile. In any case, individuals have utilized chamomile for a considerable length of time as a characteristic solution for anxiety without agony or any antagonistic side effects. By and large, chamomile is safe and powerful, and comes in pill form too, for individuals who would rather not drink tea.

L-THEANINE (GREEN TEA)

L-theanine (gamma-ethylamino-L-glutamic acid) is the transcendent amino acid in green tea leaves. Many individuals do find relief from anxiety by drinking diverse herbal teas; however, the question is, how does green tea and its L-theanine content help you with your fight against stress and anxiety?

While black tea contains L-theanine too, green tea is known to contain the most copious levels of L-theanine, making it a standout beverage everywhere throughout the world. For a long time, green tea has been utilized as a natural remedy for treating a wide assortment of health issues, such as diminishing stress and anxiety.

An investigation initiated by Dr. Hihehiko Yokogoshi in Shizuoka, Japan uncovered that L-theanine can build dopamine levels. Dopamine is a neurotransmitter that influences our feelings and inclinations. It was additionally demonstrated that the levels of GABA (Gamma Aminobutyric Acid) which are responsible for feelings of well-being were expanded after L-theanine consumption.

The fat dissolvability of L-theanine empowers it to fuse effortlessly into our brain through one of its transport systems so it can cross the blood-brain barrier. Once these L-theanine compounds are consumed by the brain, our body begins to show a few positive physiological impacts including:

- **Profound Relaxation:** Studies have shown the capacity of L-theanine to advance the generation of alpha waves in the mind. At the point when these alpha waves are enacted, we encounter a condition of profound relaxation both rationally and physically while being wakeful and totally attentive as well.

- **Non-Drowsiness:** The brain's pattern after a person has taken green tea is very similar to that of a person doing meditation. This indicates that L-theanine can influence you to feel loose without that feeling of sluggishness experienced after taking Valerian root, Kava-Kava or St. John's Wort.

- **Focused:** L-theanine can likewise help you to center more on a specific task while fighting off any symptoms of stress and anxiety. These advantages of L-theanine can be experienced as soon as thirty minutes after consumption.

L-theanine and green tea extract have been broadly utilized in Japan in various foods and drinks. In the United States, the FDA considers L-theanine an exceptionally safe constituent of green tea, because it was certified after a few toxicology research studies. The FDA included L-theanine on the GRAS (Generally Recognized as Safe) list. It is likewise considered compelling in boosting your immune system, advancing focus, improving learning abilities, and in bringing down blood pressure levels.

L-theanine significantly affects the discharge or depletion of neurotransmitters such as serotonin and dopamine, bringing about enhanced memory and learning capacity. So whenever your stress and anxiety levels are at an untouched height, gift yourself with some green tea and experience its calming impacts.

HOPS

Hops are the female flowers from the hop plant, Humulus lupulus. They're generally found in lager or beer, where they are the major source of its bitter flavor. Hops have a long history of utilization in natural medicine, going back as far as the ninth century in Europe. They have generally been utilized to treat an assortment of illnesses extending from acid reflux to severe sickness. When hops turned into an imperative element for brew producers, researchers started contemplating the impacts they could have on the body. Popular regions of study included hops' potential value for treating sleep disorders. While more research is required, studies recommend that hops may help enhance sleep quality.

A blend of hops and valerian root can also be utilized as a tranquilizer. Hops and valerian root are two powerful herbs that are ordinarily used to help ease insomnia and calm the sensory system. Hops flowers are generally utilized as a principal constituent in beer production and contain naturally occurring sedative properties. Note that valerian root is also an herb that has been utilized for centuries to improve sleep and calm anxious disorders. Consolidated, these two herbs make an intense supplement that can help you unwind, sleep peacefully, and ease mental conditions like anxiety and apprehensive tension. The fundamental and distinctive advantages of taking the Hop-Valerian supplement are:

- **Healthier Sleep:** A while back, recounted proof started to develop that hops can possibly improve sleep. In Europe, individuals observed that field laborers who cultivate hop plants tended to nod off at work more than expected. Their work was no more physically demanding than any other hands on work, so individuals started speculating whether hops had sedative properties. Early research investigations found no strong proof to suggest that hops have a sleep-actuating potential. Not long ago, though, specialists investigated hops and its impact on anxiety and sleep disorders and these studies found that hops do have sedative impacts.

As indicated by the National Institute of Health's Office of Dietary Supplements, a clinical report demonstrated that participants who took a mix of 60mg of valerian and 30mg of hops encountered a noteworthy change in the time it took to fall asleep, as well as in their quality of sleep, and they also encountered less night-time awakening than those who took a placebo. An investigation by M. Schmitz and M. Jackel of the Austrian Institut fur Psychosomatik demonstrated that individuals experiencing sleep disorders as indicated by DSM-IV criteria had a generous change in the nature of their sleep when utilizing a valerian-hops blend. The blend of these two herbs may lighten sleep disorders, for instance, insomnia, by calming the sensory system and developing a feeling of relaxation in your body and mind.

- **Mental Relaxation:** Hops and valerian both sedate the central nervous system, providing an improved feeling of peace and tranquility amid times of stress. As indicated by the University of Maryland Medical Center, studies show that hops have proven to be effective at reducing stress by expanding the quantity of gamma aminobutyric acid (GABA), which is a soothing substance. Hops is effective because it generates a soothing substance; methylbutenol, which is created over time in the dried flowers. The blend of these herbs can give you a soothing feeling following a stressful day, or ease anxiety and apprehensive tension.

- **Muscle Relaxation:** Hops can be utilized alone or in combination with valerian, as a muscle relaxant for over-stressed muscles, hardened joints and muscle fitness. According to Matthew Wood in his book "The Earth-wise Herbal: A Complete Guide to Old World Medicinal Plants," the blend of these two herbs can alleviate and unwind tense muscles, relieve muscle tension and jerking, and tremors and pain. Keep in mind to not ingest this supplement with other muscle relaxants or while driving, as it can cause extraordinary sluggishness.

VALERIAN ROOT

Valerian root is a plant, Valeriana officinalis, 3–5 feet tall, whose numerous species grow in calm and mild-to-warm atmospheres all through the world. It is most ordinarily used for its sedative-like and sleep inducing properties, and it has also been utilized to reduce anxiety. The root of the valerian plant is the main source of its medicinal use. Indigenous to parts of Asia and Europe, valerian has an antiquated history of pharmaceutical use that extends back over 1,000 years.

Besides being used to treat sleep disorders, it is also used to treat apprehension, restlessness, and anxiety. The chemical components of this herb are slightly different according to the species. Nonetheless, all assortments contain alanine, glutamine, arginine, and GABA. Different activities have been recorded when the valerian herb has been ingested, among which are improvement of GABA transmission and impacts on serotonin by means of 5-HTP.

Valerian is frequently utilized as part of a blend of different herbs that have calming impacts. To help sleep issues, valerian is often combined with hops. Hops is the plant that is best known as a constituent in brewing beer and like valerian, hops has additionally been in use for a long time as a herbal solution in regard to sleep issues, anxiety, peevishness, edginess, and fretfulness.

Hops likewise function to improve GABA levels in the brain. Research additionally shows that the calming impacts of hops may originate from its capacity to bring down body temperature. Bringing down body temperature results in languor, and it's an essential part of the body's sleep process. Researchers are presently studying how valerian root and hops work in the body, helping us find out about different ways these herbs may help sleep, disposition, and different conditions.

Valerian root basically works as an anxiolytic. Anxiolytics diminish anxiety and have calm, sedative impacts. How does valerian reduce anxiety and improve relaxation? One way it does is by expanding levels of GABA (gamma-aminobutyric acid) in the brain. GABA is a chemical that our brains normally make. GABA is what's known as an "inhibitory neurotransmitter," meaning it calms the action of the neurons in the central nervous system, which helps bring down anxiety and lift feelings of relaxation and calm. GABA is a vital neurochemical for sleep. Solid levels of GABA improve and enhance sound and tranquil sleep, and help guarantee that we expend the perfect measure of energy in moderate wave sleep and REM sleep, the two most profound and most rationally and physically therapeutic sleep stages.

Valerian root has an exceptionally distinct smell that many individuals (myself included) find unfriendly. Search for valerian in a pill or tincture to avoid this stinky odor. It isn't prescribed for those taking anti-anxiety medications, kids under twelve, or pregnant ladies. The U.S. Food and Drug Administration (FDA) marks valerian root as "generally recognized as safe" (GRAS), however, gentle reactions have been accounted for. Conceivable side effects include:

- Cerebral pain (Headache)

- Discombobulation (Dizziness)

- Stomach irritation

- Anxiety

Just like most herbal items and supplements in the US, valerian root items aren't regulated well by the FDA. Valerian root can make you lazy, so don't drive or operate machinery after ingesting it.

LEMON BALM

Lemon balm (Melissa officinalis), which falls in the category of the mint family, is viewed as a calming herb. It has been in use for as far back as the Middle Ages to alleviate stress and anxiety, stimulate sleep, enhance craving, and relief pain and distress from heartburn. Even before medieval times, lemon balm was saturated with wine to lift the spirits, help mend wounds, and treat venomous creepy crawly chomps and stings. Nowadays, lemon balm is frequently joined with other calming, alleviating herbs like valerian root, chamomile, and hops to stimulate relaxation. It is likewise utilized in creams to treat mouth blisters.

Lemon Balm is also a memory boosting, anti-anxiety nootropic otherwise called Melissa officinalis. As an herb from the mint family, it is considered a calming herb that has been utilized for a long time in medicinal settings. Recent investigations indicate the use of Lemon Balm as a cognitive enhancer with the ability to enhance processing speed and memory. In spite of the fact that it is indigenous to Europe, the herb is presently grown everywhere throughout the world for use as a natural-based supplement.

Lemon balm has become not just an herb planted to draw in honey bees, but additionally, a vital item in crops for medicine, beauty care products and furniture polish. The plant grows up to two feet high and can grow even taller if not well kept. In the spring and summer, groups of little, light yellow flowers develop where the leaves meet the stem. The leaves are profoundly wrinkled and go from dull green to yellowish-green, depending upon the soil and atmosphere. If by any chance you rub the leaves, you'll perceive a whiff of tart and sweets analogous to lemon on your fingers. The leaves are comparative, fit as a fiddle to mint leaves, and originate from a similar plant family.

Lemon balm has been endorsed as a characteristic solution for anxiety and insomnia since old Greek times. It has likewise been perceived by Commission E of the German Federal Institute for Drugs and Health Devices for its viability in treating nervous sleeping disorders and functional gastrointestinal grumblings. Conventional Moroccan medicine depicts lemon balm as having calming effects and properties that strengthen the heart. The European Scientific Cooperative prescribed Lemon Balm as a Phytotherapy for stress, touchiness and anxiety.

Lemon Balm Tea is one the most well-known solutions for insomnia and anxiety in Europe. Furthermore, Lemon balm has also been utilized by botanists to soothe stomach-related distresses, nerve pain, insomnia, headache, heart palpitations and other symptoms related to stress and anxiety. Numerous studies have demonstrated that lemon balm joined with other calming herbs, can alleviate anxiety and stimulate sleep.

Scarcely any studies have inspected lemon balm independently, however, with the exception of topical use. In one study of individuals with minor sleep problems, 81 percent of the individuals who took a herbal blend of valerian root and lemon balm indicated sleeping much better than individuals who took a placebo treatment. It isn't clear from this and other research studies whether lemon balm or valerian root (or the blend) is in charge of the outcome. The same is valid for studies on anxiety, which utilized a blend of herbs to alleviate symptoms.

A large number of researchers around the globe with published information have affirmed the advantages of lemon balm in treating stress, anxiety and insomnia. Lemon balm is indeed a valuable free gift of nature. It diminishes the negative impacts of stress and helps enhance the quality of our life.

PASSIONFLOWER (PASSIFLORA INCARNATA)

Passionflower is an herb native to southeastern United States, Argentina, and Brazil. It is a woody vine with flowers and has been eaten since antiquated times because of its implied calming and anxiolytic properties. It is sold in different forms such as powder, capsules, tablets or drops, and promoted as a treatment for sleep disorders, anxious tension, and anxiety. Commission E, framed by Germany's Federal Health Agency, affirms the internal utilization of passionflower for nervous restlessness, and the British Herbal Compendium demonstrates its utilization for apprehensive stress, sleep disorders, restlessness, and anxiety. The element of action in Passionflower is not well known; however, monoamine oxidase inhibition and actuation of GABA receptors might be included.

This excellent blooming vine was traditionally utilized by Native Americans to treat insomnia and anxiety. It was taken back to Europe and is presently grown widely and utilized therapeutically as well. Studies have observed it to be as useful for treating generalized anxiety disorder as the prescription sedative Serax (oxazepam). It is established to work by expanding brain levels of GABA.

Passionflower is best for mild anxiety, but might be valuable for individuals with extreme symptoms. It decreases tension, assists with sleep issues and is extraordinary when compared to other herbs for nerves. It calms the nerves which mitigates mood swings and headaches. In the event that you are presently taking any MAOIs, passionflower should be avoided.

While herbal remedies frequently deliver positive outcomes, recognizing the dynamic constituents can be an issue. Accordingly, users of herbal remedies might ingest insufficient or perhaps poisonous substances along with the active, anxiolytic constituents. Slightly unfavorable effects were noted in a single report which included being dizzy, sleepy and confused.

GOTU KOLA

Gotu kola is a relaxant herb with a long history of natural solutions for conditions influencing the brain and the entire body. It is a prominent natural remedy native to Asia, with misconceptions about it held by a vast majority of individuals in the west. "Kola" makes a lot of people assume that it contains caffeine. However, gotu kola is a relaxant that contains no caffeine at all. In addition, it's occasionally mistaken for another herbal remedy that offers a similar basic name. Gotu kola is both an essential traditional herb and an adaptable cooking ingredient.

Gotu kola is an enduring groundcover in the same category of plant family as parsley and carrots. It is grown copiously in the wetlands of Asia, South Africa, and Australia. It is also an essential herbal remedy to Indonesian, Chinese, and Indian Ayurvedic solutions; its health advantages are truly amazing. In customary Chinese medication, gotu kola is accepted to increase life span and, as a result, it is referred to by the Chinese as the "fountain of youth." It has been utilized to treat disorders of the brain including mental fatigue, depression, anxiety, insomnia, and memory loss. Yogis have utilized it as a meditating aid and it has been believed to reestablish equilibrium to the left and right hemispheres of the brain. Regarding the physical body, it's been utilized for colds, diarrhea, asthma, fever, hepatitis, syphilis, and stomach ulcers. It has even been utilized as a remedy for wind chomps, arsenic poisoning and toxic mushrooms. According to research, gotu kola stimulates serenity, happiness and readiness, and alleviates symptoms of anxiety and depression. The following are the areas where gotu kola can help enhance your general well-being and mental prosperity.

- It helps support cognitive capacity; it's likewise taken as a cognitive enhancer to stop memory loss. It contains ingredients that hinder the breakdown of acetylcholine; the brain chemical of learning and memory.

- It functions as an anti-depressant.

- It helps alleviate stress and anxiety; it can bring down symptoms of anxiety and stress in people experiencing generalized anxiety disorder.

- It enhances blood flow and diminishes bloating.

Given its apparent capacity to treat stress, anxiety and depression, gotu kola may likewise be utilized to treat the insomnia that occasionally goes with these illnesses. Some view this natural remedy as safe, in contrast to physician-endorsed pharmaceuticals used to treat insomnia and other sleep disorders. While more seasoned research suggests that gotu kola can aid in treating sleep disorders, additional studies are required to affirm these discoveries.

For the most part, gotu kola is very much endured. It can cause stomach irritation, headache and wobbliness. When using, begin with a low dosage and progressively increase to a full dosage, in order to reduce the probability of experiencing any side effects. Gotu kola should be administered for only two to six weeks at any given moment. Make certain to take a two-week break before resuming dosage. Gotu kola is not suitable for ingestion if you're pregnant, breastfeeding, have hepatitis or other liver disease. It is also not appropriate for individuals who have a scheduled surgery within two weeks. It should not be given to individuals presently on diuretics or prescriptions like sedatives for sleep or anxiety.

Gotu kola is safe to a great degree. It has been eaten as a nourishing food and taken as a tea by a huge number of individuals for centuries. For anti-anxiety alleviation alongside cognitive upgrades, gotu kola supplement is an effective option.

GINKGO (GINKGO BILOBA)

Ginkgo (Ginkgo biloba) is one of the most established living tree species. Most ginkgo substances are made with extracts from its fan-like leaves. The most effective parts of ginkgo are believed to be flavonoids, which have effective antioxidant qualities, and terpenoids, which help enhance circulation by expanding blood vessels and decreasing the "stickiness" of platelets.

Most of the research on ginkgo concentrates on its impact on memory, dementia and pain caused by limited blood flow (claudication). Throughout the years, there have been clashing reports with regards to the adequacy of this prominent herb in battling anxiety. There is a lot of research that demonstrates that ginkgo biloba can incredibly enhance blood flow to the brain, which regularly brings about mood enhancement and can reduce the impact of depression. This herb has been generally utilized for a considerable length of time to treat a large number of mental issues, such as, depression, Alzheimer's, Lyme disease and dementia. When testing the viability of this herb, a particular research discovered that it reduces stress and anxiety levels. By enhancing blood flow to the brain, ingesting ginkgo biloba results in less depression, enhanced cognitive capacity, alleviates headaches, and feelings of anxiety. Research on the impact of Ginkgo on memory has had differing outcomes. While some results propose that ginkgo extracts may support memory capacity in adults, other studies demonstrate that ginkgo does not enhance memory, thoughtfulness or brain work.

While ginkgo seems, by all accounts, to be safe in moderate doses, research doesn't bolster consumption of the supplement to counteract or reduce dementia or increase cognition. Additionally, more research is required to discover what part ginkgo may play in supporting brain function and treating different conditions.

Ginkgo biloba is easily procured and is generally accessible as an extract, oral tablet, capsule and tea. Crude or cooked ginkgo seeds should not be eaten for they can be noxious. Make certain to purchase from a trusted brand that is known for high quality as a few brands utilize ginkgo grown with pesticides.

KAVA (KAVA-KAVA)

Kava was customarily prepared as a relaxing beverage from the rhizome of the kava plant (Piper methysticum) among Pacific Island societies. In the course of recent decades, kava has picked up ubiquity in Western nations as a result of its anxiolytic and sedative properties. The putative dynamic standards of kava extracts include a few kava-lactones, which may indirectly empower the binding of GABA receptors and may expand the quantity of GABA's binding sites. Research indicates that Kava may apply its properties through its activities on sodium and calcium voltage dependent channels.

This herb has a long history of utilization among native Polynesians. It has gentle, unwinding compounds and when utilized in high dosages, has a practically inebriating impact. According to research, kava is equivalent to physician recommended meds of the benzodiazepine class for treating anxiety disorders.

Be that as it may, it is not at all like medical sedatives; kava is known for its calming impact without the average cognitive fluffiness or debilitation.

As a drink, kava has been used in many societies for a considerable length of time since it is known to ease restlessness, insomnia and anxiety. The engaging quality of kava is that it is anxiolytic yet not sedative or mentally impairing, which are the typical side effects of benzodiazepines. The biochemical mechanism of kava's anxiolytic action has been postulated to happen through improved ligand fusing with GABA type-A receptors, blockage of violated-gated sodium channels and calcium particle channels, dopamine and norepinephrine reuptake inhibition, and reversible inhibition of monoamine oxidase (MAO) B.

Although Kava is normally extracted from the root of the herb, the vital compounds are likewise present in the leaves and stems of the herb. A double-blind study was conducted in 1996 to treat 29 subjects who had been diagnosed as having a general anxiety disorder with a kava extract three times daily for a month (100 mg dosages given 3 times every day). At the point of comparison with the placebo treatment group, the individuals who took kava found that their anxiety symptoms were fundamentally diminished, and there were no unfavorable side effects revealed or noted. Indeed, unfavorable responses to kava are uncommon, so you can ingest kava with assurance.

Kava does not blend well with other herbal-based remedies that can cause sluggishness, such as 5-HTP, gotu kola, valerian root, and melatonin. It should also never be ingested with anti-anxiety prescriptions, anti-depressants, and sleeping pills. You may have heard that kava is connected to liver damage; however, this issue has been exposed and is, to a great extent, unwarranted. Kava is accessible in the United States as a fluid tincture or capsule, and to a lesser degree, as a tea. A word of caution: Kava has been associated to reports of serious liver toxicity in the past leading to its temporary removal from the market and subsequent return. Hence, it should not be considered by anyone with a history of liver disease.

ASHWAGANDHA
(WITHANIA SOMNIFERA)

Ashwagandha is popularly known as Indian ginseng, a bush plant from the nightshade (Solanaceae) family. The root, leaves and berries of ashwagandha have been utilized by conventional Indian Ayurvedic medications for centuries to alleviate nerve tissue impairment, sexual issues, inflammation, stress, anxiety, insomnia and different numerous sicknesses. The name ashwagandha originates from the Sanskrit words ashva, which means horse, and gandha, which means smell. In reality, ashwagandha is known for having a horse like odor, and the name may likewise allude to the conviction that ingesting ashwagandha gives you the quality and virility of a steed.

Meanwhile, in recent times, ashwagandha has been examined as an adaptogenic, anxiolytic, antioxidant, antidepressant, cardioprotector, immunoregulating, anti-inflammatory, antibacterial, antifungal, neuroprotector, and cognitive-improving compound. Given its stress-diminishing impacts, it's not shocking that Ashwagandha is likewise often utilized as a sedative. In fact, many individuals utilize ashwagandha supplements to enhance sleep quality and prepare their psyche for sleeping.

An exceptional way ashwagandha will aid sleep is through antagonizing extracellular calcium, which decreases mind cell excitation. Calcium excitation has all the earmarks of being associated with anxiety and other mental conditions; this implies that diminishing it can bring about an anxiolytic (anxiety-decreasing) effect. Ashwagandha is superlatively known as an adaptogen: an herb that enables the body to oppose a wide assortment of physiological and mental stressors. Adaptogens bolster the body's capacity to react to stress strongly and can hypothetically help with a wide assortment of health concerns. As for sleep, research proposes that ashwagandha supplements appear to lessen stress and anxiety, enabling the body to settle down and get ready for sleep. Moreover, ashwagandha seems to enhance the quality of sleep. There are additionally some indications that ashwagandha can help with insomnia, however more studies are required.

For a considerable length of time, ashwagandha has been used not only to treat infections and fevers, but additionally, to improve the state of mind, diminish anxiety and depression, fight panic attacks and reduce insomnia. A clue to the calming impact of ashwagandha can be found in the second piece of its botanical name, Withania somnifera; the word emerges from the Latin word "somnus," or sleep.

As indicated by medicinal specialists, ashwagandha owes its relaxant properties to a group of alkaloids called, withanolides. Additional constituents include different alkaloids called sitoindosides, alongside saponins and grouped minerals which likewise play a vital part in delivering relaxation. Ashwagandha fills in as a depressant on the central nervous system, causing vibes of serenity and relaxation, which makes sleep simpler to accomplish.

Ashwagandha is by all accounts a safe, natural sedative. It is supported not just by centuries of traditional practice, but in addition, a decent number of current clinical research trials. It has been observed to be moderately safe and successful at enhancing sleep quality both when measured directly, or indirectly through stress and anxiety diminishment. Ashwagandha is currently being experimentally explored as a helpful device for a wide assortment of health trepidations.

LAVENDER

Lavender is naturally grown in dry, bright, rough ranges and is native to the Mediterranean. France is believed to be the world's pioneer of lavender exchange; however, it can be grown anywhere, provided that you select the correct assortment and give it perfect growing conditions. Traced back to as far as 2,500 years ago, this delightfully scented herb has been utilized in the following ways: disinfectant, antiperspirant, perfume, sexual enhancer and bug repellant. Lavender smells great, as well as enables you to look and feel extraordinary! This fragrant herb has been utilized to treat skin injuries, calm anxiety and bolster your immune system.

It will intrigue you to realize that lavender was additionally utilized in old times to tame lions and tigers. It calms anxiety and promotes stress alleviation. In addition, lavender also has a considerable rundown of therapeutic properties, making it a characteristic well-being whiz. Lavender is recently gaining prominence as an alternative to regular medication treatments.

Lavender is well known as a calming and unwinding herb and has been utilized for insomnia, natural stress alleviation, depression and anxiety. A recent study found that the fragrance of lavender increases with the time you spend in profound (moderate wave) sleep; however, the effects were more grounded in ladies than in men. One other discovery proposed that lavender diminishes the severity of depression when taken simultaneously with an antidepressant. While lavender fragrance-based treatment can help with your sleep and disposition, it additionally has an extensive variety of health advantages.

All through history, individuals have turned to lavender for a wide range of illnesses, such as skin disorders, stomach-related protestations, acne treatment, pain alleviation and prevention, and treatment of infections. Although a significant part of the proof that backs the therapeutic utilization of lavender is recounted, researchers are beginning to examine the impacts of lavender on the body and have found that lavender has anti-fungal, anti-microbial, and anti-inflammatory properties. Lavender has additionally appeared to diminish the movement of candida albicans and might be a compelling treatment for different diseases. Aromatherapists feel that lavender oil is currently one of the most resourceful oils ever due to its many recuperating properties, and believe it to be one of the finest oils to have in your possession.

Lavender is currently been utilized in the following areas:

- Pain alleviation

- Migraine and headaches

HERBAL-BASED REMEDIES

- Muscle hurts and sprains

- Relaxation

- Restlessness

- Depression

- Stimulating sleep

- Muscle relaxant

- Stomach-related distress, gas and colic

- Aggravation

- Asthma

- Bug nibbles

- Allergies

- Menstrual spasms

- Burns

- Dry skin

- Skin break out treatment

- Creepy crawly repellant

- Chicken Pox

- Dermatitis

A few ways of utilizing lavender as an essential oil may be:

- Blend 4 to 6 drops of Lavender essential oil in your bath water if you have dry skin.

- Diffuse 10 to 12 drops of Lavender into the air in the process of your workday for natural stress alleviation.

- For every ounce of your most loved, delicately scented, unrefined natural oil (olive oil), include 2 drops of Lavender oil, which transforms it into a body oil with all the advantages of lavender oil to enhance your skin, unwind your brain, ward off creepy crawlies, and stimulate sleep.

- The unrefined natural oil you mix it with functions as a carrier oil for lavender, which dilutes the oil and conveys the valuable properties into your skin.

- You might need to utilize this oil as a replacement for your body moisturizer if it contains chemicals or other added substances. This is because when you put something on your skin, it seeps into your body. It's critical to select healthy oils to put on your skin.

- You can likewise utilize the fragrant dried flowers of lavender to make magnificent scented sachets. As an herbal alternative to mothballs, add the sachets to your drawers and storerooms. Obviously, this gives an additional advantage of soothing lavender fragrance-based treatment to your clothing, too!

Commercially, lavender is now in numerous individual care items; however, it is in trace quantities and is usually mixed with chemicals that are not perfect for your skin or your well-being. If you intend to use lavender for a variety of functions, it can be found quite readily; it is accessible, crisp, dried and powdered, and also available as an essential oil. Essential oils are concentrated extracts from the plant, making them over 50 times more powerful than the plant itself! Lavender essential oil has such a huge number of advantages that it can serve as a magnificent piece of your natural well-being and way of life. All things considered, if lavender could tame lions and tigers, imagine what it would do for you during a typical day at the office!

RHODIOLA (RHODIOLA ROSEA)

Rhodiola is a herb grown in high elevations such as the mountains of Siberia and Northwestern China. It is one of a handful of herbs that grows in freezing temperatures. The root of this herb is the source of the constituents used in making the supplement. It is likewise known as Golden Root, Siberian Root, Roseroot, or Arctic Root. It has been used for quite a long time to help individuals who are experiencing anxiety and stress. As a capable adaptogen, Rhodiola builds the body's protection and immunity to stress while normalizing bodily activities.

Rhodiola reinforces the body against the stresses that influence us in our day-to-day activities, regardless of whether they are physical or mental, at home or at work. Whatever the reason might be, Rhodiola encourages you to adapt and additionally keeps your body from going into an over-burdened state where more serious conditions can occur. Multiple studies have demonstrated that Rhodiola gives a tremendous lift to the body and mind. In a particular study of individuals with stress-related fatigue conducted in Sweden, Rhodiola exerted an "anti-fatigue" impact, expanded mental performance, diminished the stress hormone cortisol in the blood, and decreased stress in general. In another research study detailed in The Journal of Alternative and Complementary Medicine, Rhodiola triggered changes in patients with generalized anxiety disorder. However another investigation of depressed individuals in Armenia indicated a noteworthy change in general mood because of taking Rhodiola extract.

More than 300 human-based studies on Rhodiola demonstrated that the herb has anti-anxiety, anti-stress and anti-depressant properties, and taking the extract of the root creates no huge negative impacts. This is in clear contrast to other medications for similar purposes, which commonly cause sleep disorders, stomach-related irritation, and an assortment of mood disorders.

Unlike numerous other herbs, Rhodiola produces a substantial experience. Whenever you ingest this herb, you'll feel it. Ordinarily, users report improved vitality, enhanced inclination, enormously diminished stress, better sleep, and enhanced sexual strength. These impacts are generally due to a novel group of compounds in the root known as rosavins. The rosavins act in the brain in an assortment of ways to relax the body.

In general, Rhodiola has shown more noteworthy adequacy and safety than pharmaceutical medications for anxiety, depression and fatigue.

SCHISANDRA

This herb originated from a vine in China and parts of Russia. It is also known as Schisandra or Schisandra Chinensis, and its berry is utilized as a type of traditional Chinese medication. The Schisandra organic product is otherwise called the Five Flavor Berry since its taste catches the five noteworthy flavors: sweet, salty, bitter, and spicy. This healthy and colorful berry is classified as an adaptogen, which averts physical and chemical stress on the body. Whenever it enters the body, it collects in the heart, kidneys, brain, lungs, and generally in liver tissues.

Schisandra is commonly utilized as a performance enhancer and a treatment for different diseases. Antioxidants present in the Schisandra's natural product prompt its remedial, protective, and life-improving properties that stimulate general well-being. It is a valuable and helpful herb for health problems that are identified with stress and has a decent impact in helping those with depression both physically and emotionally. This herb has many capable functions in the body, including expanding your stamina and physical endurance.

Schisandra is outstanding for its activity to alleviate stress, and is additionally a decent herb that helps the liver to mend. This herb is a natural health remedy that is known to help reduce fatigue by invigorating the DNA, building power, and also strengthening the cells and body tissues. Its adaptogenic nature makes it a phenomenal antioxidant, with qualities that will help your cognitive forces and capacity to think clearly and may also expand your memory. As one of the adaptogenic herbs, and in the same manner as different adaptogens, the active constituents contained in the schisandra natural product will bolster your ability to neutralize the impacts of stress and fatigue. This herb is very calming and as such, using it will ease anxiety. This makes it one of the most common healthy insomnia remedies.

It can be utilized to help with healing some of the issues caused by stress, including:

- Adrenal gland depletion

- Insomnia

- Headaches

- Dizziness

- Palpitations

- Excessive sweating

Many of these symptoms are ordinarily caused by emotionally-based stress. The schisandra berry can be utilized to help with adrenal exhaustion syndrome, which is regularly caused or aggravated by chronic stress. If by any chance you have been encountering chronic stress symptoms, you may find that your immune system is currently less able to battle infections. The schisandra herb has a decent method of helping the parts of the immune system most regularly affected by progressive, chronic stress. This herb is useful in combating problems that involve both immune health and long term chronic stress. These problems include colds and influenza symptoms, and it's additionally useful for the improvement of your immune system.

Many individuals don't have the foggiest idea how stress influences their well-being and how it causes them a large number of health problems. The schisandra herb is known to be very helpful to individuals experiencing adrenal fatigue. It works by supporting and enhancing the strength of the adrenal glands, which in turn alleviates the symptoms of adrenal fatigue. Schisandra is more effective when used with different adaptogens, such as reishi mushroom, eleuthero root, licorice root, Panax ginseng, American ginseng, cordyceps and rhodiola rosea root. If you experience difficulty in sleeping, utilizing this herb is a healthy approach that can help you, particularly if your insomnia is stress related.

BACOPA MONNIERI (BRAHMI)

Bacopa monnieri is an herbal nootropic supplement that naturally boosts brain power and reduces anxiety. Native to ancient India, bacopa monnieri is an essential medicinal herb that has been improving mood, learning ability, memory, and brain health for centuries. It is one of the oldest and most regarded of the nootropic supplements. Sometimes referred to as Brahmi, this traditional Ayurvedic medicine has a centuries old history of being a potent stress reliever, cognitive enhancer, and brain protectant. It is viable for improving memory formation and speedy recall, enhancing clarity of thought, and escalating overall brain function. Research proves it has the potential to serve as a treatment for dementia.

Bacopa is also believed to have significant anxiolytic effects, creating a feeling of calmness and serenity, and decreasing feelings of stress. It is a sensational general relaxant and can enhance the quality of sleep, so the user wakes up feeling rested and renewed. It has nootropic effects similar to those of Piracetam, one of the most common chemically synthesized smart medications, however bacopa monnieri is a herbal-based supplement that is synthesized in nature, made from the extract of the bacopa monnieri plant, a low-growing perennial indigenous to southern India and also found in warm wetlands all over Asia and southern states in the U.S.

It is utilized all over Asia as a traditional treatment in a diverse variety of disorders from indigestion to ulcers, asthma, and even epilepsy; however, it is basically known in the west for its powerful nootropic properties.

- **Enhanced Learning Faculty:** Bacopa Monnieri is well-known for escalating cognitive processing, thereby aiding easier and faster learning of new concepts and ideas. Research shows that it significantly enhances spatial learning. Taking bacopa while studying can assist easier and faster assimilation and recollection of new materials. Reports borne out by trials at India's Central Drug Institute (CDI) in Lucknow indicate that children taking bacopa exhibit improved academic capabilities.

- **Memory Enhancement:** One of the most powerful benefits of bacopa monnieri is enhancing memory; both in formation and speed of recall. Studies show it significantly improved memory in groups of people, and more research is ongoing concerning the likelihood of using bacopa monnieri to treat memory-impaired neurological disorders.

- **Stress Relief and Anxiety Reduction:** An important benefit of bacopa monnieri is its ability to alleviate anxiety and reduce the symptoms of stress. Research demonstrated that Bacopa significantly reduced anxiety and depression in volunteers, and studies with animals compare Bacopa favorably to other herbal extracts as an effective remedy for the treatment of anxiety and other mental disorders

- **Mood Management and Anti-Anxiety Actions:** Bacopa monnieri creates its calming effects through a series of actions. Modulating the activities of specific neurotransmitter receptors is one of the most important anti-anxiety effects, including those that control the uptake of serotonin, which is strongly connected to anxiety and mood management. Additionally, hersaponin is one of bacopa's functional ingredients; an alkaloid that has been shown to have a relaxing, sedative effect. Research has shown that another of bacopa's functional ingredients, Bacoside-A can prevent dopamine receptor dysfunction, a potent neurotransmitter liable for the brain's pleasure and reward systems, which is closely related to mood. The functional ingredients present in bacopa are also known to aid the activities of GABA, a very strong inhibitory neurotransmitter that acts to stave off anxiety by confining the firing of neurons that are over-excited by stress.

Bacopa monnieri is a potent herbal supplement that can make a significant positive difference in how you think, learn, and feel; however, taking the right dose is very important. Unlike racetam-class nootropics and other chemical smart medications that are colossally well tolerated at very high dosages, bacopa has the potential to be very toxic when taken in large dosages. It is also not like many other nootropics that are generally slow-acting and do not have immediate observable effects. Achieving significant benefits from

Bacopa might require a prolonged regimen of frequent doses over the course of four to six weeks. Just like any other herbal supplement, it is reasonable to start with the lowest possible effective dose and gradually increase as required, closely observing the reactions and effects and making required adjustments based on your observations.

Bacopa monnieri is adequately effective on its own; however, it has been considered by users to be at its best when combined with other nootropics. It is regularly combined with other herbal-based supplements for general health reasons, but in the case of mood management and cognitive enhancement, it rounds out practically any nootropic stack. If you're stacking for a calming effect or for additional energy and cognitive stimulation, adding a good choline can be very important in achieving maximum benefit and staving off side effects such as a headache.

Generally, bacopa monnieri is considered safe and effective, but there are some potential side effects ranging from minor to somewhat serious. The most familiar side effects include:

- Indigestion

- Dry mouth

- Fatigue

- Increased bowel movements

These are all minor side effects and often stop occurring as the body becomes accustomed to bacopa. More severe potential side effects include:

- Thyroid disorders

- Gastrointestinal tract blockage

- Urinary tract problems

It also has a negative effect on ulcers, lung conditions, and slow heartbeat or bradycardia.

The safety of bacopa monnieri during pregnancy is still inadequately researched and, as such, pregnant women are advised to avoid it. A lot of the side effects are, in part, a result of dosage levels. Bear in mind to always start with the most minimal effective dose and gradually build up the dosage accordingly.

ASTRAGALUS

For centuries, the potent extract from the astragalus plant has been utilized as a traditional remedy. The extract comes from one of many species of small shrubs and plants in the astragalus genus. It is also an herb, a member of the legume family. It is particularly known to inhabitants of the northern hemisphere as locoweed or goat's thorn, hence its genus. Astragalus is very common in Chinese traditional medicine and its most common form is basically in the extract of its root, where the vital nutrients and unique constituents are most concentrated. It looks a lot like tree bark in its natural, unpowdered form.

Due to certain claims that it is both an adaptogenic and an anti-aging substance, this herbal supplement has recently become very popular and highly sought after. Its adaptogenic nature enables it to actually transform the chemical nature of the body and assist it to adapt to different stimuli, which makes the body healthier. Astragalus is very much available in many countries in the world. Below are some of its many benefits:

- **Boosts Immune System:** Apart from being an antioxidant, which aids in the protection of the immune system from major attacks, the quality of adaptogens in astragalus can actually assist your immune system to become smarter and more effective in the way it handles any foreign pathogen and substance, which in turn boosts the general strength of your immune system from simple infections.

- **Reduces Stress:** The presence of chronic stress and high anxiety levels in your body can be very dangerous, as stress hormones can wreak havoc on your system if not kept in check. As a result of this, finding ways to relax is a necessity, and astragalus has been found to reduce levels of stress and generally promote peace and calm. If you are experiencing constant nervous tension and mood swings, astragalus can bring about equilibrium in your hormone levels.

- **Reduces Sleep Disorder:** If you're experiencing interrupted sleep patterns, sleeplessness or insomnia, frequently consuming astragalus root extract can quickly return you to a normal and healthy circadian rhythm. By enhancing metabolic efficiency, hormonal balance and overall health, astragalus can aid in delivering undisrupted, restful and serene sleep.

- **Protection for Healthy Heart:** Whilst a lot of people constantly look for ways to prevent dreaded heart conditions, the truth remains that cardiovascular cases are some of the most occurring exigent illnesses in the modern world. As a result of this, herbs such as astragalus, which has been found to guard the heart after a severe episode, such as stroke, are very valuable and are currently well sought after. Studies have demonstrated that consuming the extract of astragalus sequel to a stroke can aid to strengthen the artery walls and maintain nerve functionality of the heart. This is mostly due to the results of the antioxidant effects of this potent herb. The astragalus is a very vital herb for individuals experiencing chronic heart failure, due to its ability to prevent intervals between episodes, in hearts that are presently damaged.

- **Relief from Allergies:** People all over the world are a victim of one seasonal allergy or the other. For instance, hay fever is one which nobody seems to have a full grasp on. However, astragalus root extract shows a very promising attribute towards reducing a string of allergic reactions. While the chemical trail isn't fully understood yet, it is perceived that the chemical constituents in astragalus can wade off the release of histamines, which is one of the causes of allergic reactions. Therefore astragalus can relieve itchy eyes, runny nose and other irritating, annoying symptoms.

As good as many of these benefits are, there is an exception that can work against the body. For individuals suffering from any autoimmune disease, for instance, HIV, lupus, MS or rheumatoid arthritis, taking astragalus can actually aggravate the symptoms by boosting the activities and strength of your immune system. If by any chance you are experiencing any of the illnesses mentioned above, you are advised to avoid using this herb. Before making any major change in your health or herbal regimen, you are advised to talk to a medical professional first.

GALPHIMIA GLAUCA

Galphimia glauca is a herb extracted from a small evergreen shrub found in Mexico and other parts of Central America. While it is sometimes referred to as simply galphimia or thyallis, it is usually prepared as a homeopathic remedy and proffers a number of health benefits. Galphimia has been in use for a very long time in traditional Latin American medicine to treat asthma, allergies, mental disorders, and anxiety.

The research on the health benefits of galphimia glauca extract is still very limited. Yet, there is tangible evidence from a series of animal-based research studies that demonstrate galphimia extract can proffer anti-anxiety benefits. And a 2007 study published in Planta Medica revealed its extract can be of some use in the treatment of anxiety. According to the study, 152 individuals with generalized anxiety disorder (GAD) took either galphimia extract or the commonly prescribed anti-anxiety drug, lorazepam, every day for about four weeks. Results from the study show that there was no difference between the anxiety-reducing effect of galphimia extract and that of lorazepam.

Advocates for the health effect of homeopathic preparations of galphimia are also quite limited. The only recent research available is an older meta-analysis published in the Austrian journal Wiener Medizinische Wochenschrift in 1997. In this meta-analysis, researchers reviewed eleven clinical trials on the utilization of homeopathic preparations of galphimia for the treatment of hay fever. Generally, homeopathic preparation of galphimia indicated to be superior to the placebo treatment in alleviating eye-related symptoms, for instance, itching and watering of the eyes. More recent data on the potential health benefits of homeopathic galphimia is unavailable.

As a result of limited studies and data on galphimia, not much is known about the safety of utilizing galphimia in the long term. But there are some agitations that administering galphimia in combination with certain medications, like blood-thinning medications and central nervous system depressants may cause harmful side effects. Likewise, homeopathic preparations of galphimia might set off a number of side effects which include dry mouth and fatigue. Bear in mind that the safety of herbal supplements in pregnant women, nursing mothers, children, and individuals with medical conditions or those who are taking medications has not been categorically established. It is best to always consult your doctor before taking any kind of supplements.

HERBAL-BASED REMEDIES

Table 2: Summary of Herbal-Based Remedies

Natural Remedies	Treatment	Mechanism
Chamomile	Alleviates Stress and anxiety, Actuates Sleep, Boosts Immune System, Treats Stomach Issues, Oversees Diabetes, Eases Menstrual Discomfort, Skin and Hair Care, Treats Allergic Responses	The presence of flavonoids, sesquiterpenes, and other intense antioxidants in this tea effectively affect the body. GABA receptor binding and modification of monoamine pathways
L-Theanine (Green Tea)	Alleviates Stress and anxiety, Enhances Focus	Builds dopamine levels; dopamine is a neurotransmitter that influences our feelings and inclinations.
Hops	Ensures Better Sleep, relaxes muscles, Relaxation, Eases insomnia, Calms the sensory system, Eases mental conditions like anxiety and anxious tension	Affects your focal sensory system, advancing a feeling of calm and peace amid times of stress.
Valerian Root	Alleviates Anxiety, Peevishness, Nervousness and Agitation; Eases insomnia	Improvement of GABA transmission and also impact on serotonin by means of 5-HTP, a receptor. Basically works as an anxiolytic
Lemon Balm	Stress, Anxiety and Insomnia issues, Stomach related distresses, Nerve pain, Headache, Heart palpitations and others symptoms related with stress and anxiety.	Acts as a cognitive enhancer, able to improve processing speed and memory.
Passion Flower	Sleep disorders, anxious tension, and anxiety, nervous restlessness, apprehensive stress, Generalized anxiety disorder (GAD)	Works by expanding brain levels of GABA.
Gotu Kola	Mental fatigue, anxiety, depression, memory loss, insomnia, asthma, colds, diarrhea, fever, hepatitis, stomach ulcers, and syphilis.	It contains compounds that inhibit the breakdown of acetylcholine, the brain chemical of learning and memory. It act as an antidepressant
Ginkgo (Ginkgo Biloba)	Alzheimer's, depression, dementia, Lyme disease ; reduces Anxiety and stress levels	Flavonoids, which have powerful antioxidant qualities, and terpenoids, which help improve circulation by dilating blood vessels and reducing the "stickiness" of platelets.

Kava-Kava	Relieves anxiety, restlessness and insomnia	Kava-lactones empower the binding of GABA receptors and expand the quantity of GABA's binding sites. Apply its impacts through its activities on sodium and calcium voltage dependent channels.
Ashwagandha	Inflammation, stress, anxiety, sexual issues, nerve tissue damage, insomnia and numerous different sicknesses	Fills in as a depressant on the focal sensory system, causing vibes of serenity and relaxation, making sleep simpler to accomplish.
Lavender	Skin injuries, alleviates stress, calms anxiety, insomnia, depression, bolsters your immune system, acne treatment, skin disorders, stomach related protestations, pain alleviation, and counteracts and treat infections	Its antidepressant and Aromatherapeutic Nature
Rhodiola	Anxiety, stress, depression and fatigue	Impact is generally due to a novel group of compounds in the root known as rosavins. The rosavins act in the brain in an assortment of ways.
Schisandra	Insomnia, Stress, Adrenal gland depletion, Headaches, Dazedness, Palpitations, and Lavish Sweating	Help fatigue by invigorating the DNA and building power and strengthening the cells and body tissues. Its adaptogenic nature makes it a phenomenal antioxidant, and its qualities help your cognitive forces and capacity to think clearly and expand your memory.
Bacopa Monnieri (Brahmi)	Boosts brain power and reduces anxiety, relieves stress, helps in mood management, cognitive enhancer, and dementia.	5HT2c, metal chelation, antioxidant and anti-inflammatory effects. Possible cholinergic effects
Astragalus Membranaceous	Boosts Immune System, Reduces Stress, Reduces Sleep Disorder, Protection for Healthy Heart, and Relief from Allergies	Its adaptogenic nature enables it to actually transform the chemical nature of the body and assist it to adapt to different stimuli, which makes the body healthier
Galphimia Glauca	Asthma, allergies, mental disorders, and alleviates anxiety	Effect of homeopathic preparations of galphimia is quite limited

CHAPTER 4

NON–PHARMACOLOGICAL TREATMENTS

COGNITIVE BEHAVIORAL THERAPY: RELAXATION

Cognitive behavioral therapy (CBT) is the most generally utilized treatment for anxiety disorders. Research indicates it is a viable in the treatment of panic disorders, social anxiety disorders, fears (phobias), and generalized anxiety disorders, among other conditions.

Cognitive behavioral treatment asserts that negative examples bend our perception of the world and ourselves. As the name implies, this includes two principle segments:

- Cognitive treatment looks at how negative contemplations, or comprehensions, add to anxiety.

- Behavioral treatment inspects how you carry on and respond in circumstances that trigger anxiety.

Cognitive behavioral treatment is built on the fundamental premise that our thoughts, not external occurrences, influence the way we feel. At the end of the day, it's not the circumstance you're going through that decides how you feel, but your view of the circumstance. For instance, envision that you've quite recently been invited to a major event. Consider three diverse methods for pondering on the invite, and how those thoughts would influence your feelings.

Scenario A: A co-worker invites you to his birthday party.

Thought #1: Sounds like this party is going to be a lot of fun. I love hanging out and meeting new people!

Feelings: Happy, energized

Thought #2: Parties aren't my thing. I'd much rather remain in my apartment and watch movies.

Feelings: Neutral

Thought #3: I'll probably just make of a fool of myself if I go.

Feelings: Anxious, sad

As should be obvious, an event can prompt totally different and distinct feelings in various individuals. Everything relies upon our individual desires, mentalities and convictions. For individuals with anxiety disorders, negative methods for speculation fuel the negative feelings of anxiety and fear. The objective of cognitive behavioral therapy for anxiety is to recognize and adjust these negative thoughts and convictions. The concept is that when you change the way you think, it automatically changes the way you feel.

THOUGHT CHALLENGING IN CBT

Thought challenging otherwise called cognitive restructuring is a procedure in which you challenge the negative thinking patterns that add to your anxiety, and substitute them with more positive and sensible considerations. This process involves three stages:

1. Recognize your negative thoughts: With anxiety disorders, circumstances are seen as more perilous than they truly are. To somebody with a germ phobia, for instance, shaking someone else's hand can appear to be life threatening. Despite the fact that you may effortlessly observe this as an illogical fear, recognizing your own particular illogical, terrifying thoughts can be exceptionally difficult. One procedure is to ask yourself what you were thinking when you began feeling on edge.

2. Challenge your negative thoughts: In this second step, your therapist will show you how to assess your anxiety-inciting thoughts. This includes cross-examining the indications of your terrifying thoughts, investigating unhelpful convictions, and testing out the truth of negative expectations. The techniques for challenging negative thoughts include conducting investigations, measuring the advantages and disadvantages of stressing or keeping away from the thing you fear, and deciding on what the practical chance is that what you're restless about will actually happen.

3. Substitute negative thoughts with sensible considerations: Once you've recognized the illogical expectations and negative distortions in your restless thoughts, you can substitute them with new thoughts that are more precise and positive. Your therapist may likewise assist you to invent sensible, calming statements you can say to yourself when you're confronted, or when you expect a circumstance that typically sends your anxiety levels skyrocketing.

To see how thought challenges functions in cognitive behavioral therapy, consider the following illustration:

Jane won't take the subway since she's worried she'll blackout, and after that, everybody will believe she's insane. Her therapist has requested that she record her negative thoughts, recognize the errors or cognitive contortions in her reasoning, and concoct a more levelheaded translation. The outcomes are as follows:

Negative Thought #1: What if I blackout on the subway?

Cognitive contortion: Predicting the most exceedingly awful event

More reasonable thought: I've never blacked out, so it's far-fetched that I will do so on the subway.

Negative Thought #2: it will be terrible if I blackout!

Cognitive contortion: Blowing things far, far out of proportion

More reasonable thought: If I blackout, I'll come to in no time. That is not all that terrible.

Negative Thought #3: People will think I'm insane.

Cognitive contortion: Jumping to conclusions

More reasonable thought: People will probably be concerned and check to see if I'm alright.

Substituting negative thoughts with more reasonable ones is easier said than done. Regularly, negative thoughts are part of a long lasting pattern of thinking. It requires practice to reprieve the propensity. That is the reason cognitive behavioral therapy includes practicing on your own as well as in form of a self-help program.

RELAXATION

Our fast-paced society can make individuals push their minds and bodies as far as possible, usually to the detriment of physical and mental prosperity. As indicated by the Mind/Body Medical Institute at Harvard University, 60 to 90 percent of all therapeutic office visits in the United States are for stress-related disorders. Such stress affects well-being and the immune system. Relaxation techniques are useful instruments for adapting to stress and encouraging long term well-being by slowing down the body and calming the psyche (mind). Such techniques usually involve: refocusing attention (for instance, seeing areas of tension), expanding body mindfulness, and activities to interface the body and mind together (Meditation). If utilized every day, these practices can prompt a more advantageous point of view on stressful conditions. Truth be told, more than

3,000 studies demonstrate the valuable impacts of relaxation on mental and emotional well-being and prosperity.

RELAXATION TECHNIQUES

The following are noteworthy relaxation techniques:

Autogenic Training: This method utilizes both visual imagery and body awareness to move you into a profound state of relaxation. You envision a calm place and after that, you focus on various physical sensations, moving from the feet to the head. For instance, one may concentrate on warmth and heaviness in the limbs, simple natural breathing, or a calm heartbeat.

Breathing: In breathing techniques, you put one hand on your chest and the other on your belly. Take a moderate, full breath, sucking in as much air as you can. As you are doing this, your belly should push against your hand. Hold your breath and afterward gradually breathe out.

Dynamic muscle relaxation: This system includes gradually straining and afterward discharging each muscle group separately, beginning with the muscles in the toes and ending with those in the head.

Meditation: The two well-known types of meditation in the U.S. include Transcendental Meditation (repeating a mantra; a solitary word or expression) and Mindfulness Meditation (concentrating your attention on your thoughts and sensations).

Guided Imagery: Similar to autogenic training, guided imagery includes tuning in to a trained therapist or a guided imagery CD to move into a condition of profound relaxation. Once in a relaxed state, the images that surface in your mind can enable you to reach realizations about your spiritual, emotional, and physical well-being.

MECHANISM OF RELAXATION TECHNIQUES

When you wind up noticeably stressed, your body participates in something many refer to as the "fight-or-flight response." The fight-or-flight response alludes to changes that happen in the body when it gets ready to either fight or run. These progressions include elevated heart rate, blood pressure and rate of breathing, and a 300 to 400 percent expansion in the measure of blood being pumped to the muscles. After some time, these responses raise cholesterol levels, exasperate intestinal activities, and knock down the immune system. As a rule, they leave you feeling "stressed out."

Nevertheless, you likewise have the inverse of the fight-or-flight response, the "relaxation response." This term first came into use in the mid-1970s by a Harvard cardiologist named Herbert Benson; it alludes to changes that happen in the body when it is in a profound condition of relaxation. These progressions include low blood pressure and heart rate, muscle tension, rate of breathing, and also feelings of being calm and in charge. Learning the relaxation response helps counter the impacts of the fight-or-flight response and, after some time, permits the development of a more noteworthy state of alertness. The relaxation response can be developed through various techniques, including meditation and dynamic muscle relaxation. It is currently a prescribed treatment for some stress-related disorders.

WHY RELAXATION

Research proposes that meditation can help enhance your personal satisfaction in life and decrease stress hormone levels. Clinical investigations likewise demonstrate that relaxation techniques lessen the perception of pain. One clinical study found that among patients experiencing colorectal surgery, the individuals who listened to guided imagery tapes before, amid, and after the operation had less pain and required less pain meds than the individuals who did not. Another found that relaxation practices, for instance, deep breathing, dynamic relaxation, and visualization, improved the immune response among breast cancer patients.

Meditation has additionally been utilized as a component in the treatment for post-traumatic stress disorder (PTSD) in Vietnam veterans, and to break substance abuse patterns in drug addicts and alcohol abusers. Relaxation techniques can likewise upgrade to adapting skills in individuals suffering from migraine to help them lessen stress, and also enhance moods in those suffering from cancers and tumors. In general, research has shown that with steady practice, relaxation techniques can conceivably decrease symptoms or enhance results in the conditions below:

- Stress

- Anxiety

- Pain

- Panic disorders

- High blood pressure

- Irritable bowel syndrome

- Infertility

- Premenstrual syndrome

- Chronic tension headaches

- High cholesterol

- Fibromyalgia

- Diabetes

- Insomnia

- Psoriasis

- Labor and Child birth

- Arthritis

- Hyperactivity in children, as in attention deficit hyperactivity disorder (ADHD)

Relaxation techniques are perceived to be exceptionally safe. In the event that you need to decrease stress, lower anxiety levels and improve general well-being, you can coach yourself using any of these relaxation techniques. It is critical that normal medical care and counsel be taken for these conditions, too. Relaxation techniques are only intended to supplement common medical care.

EXERCISE

The overall physical benefits of exercise have long been known to improve physical condition and fight diseases and, over time, physicians have encouraged staying physically active to reduce the causes of mortality. As surprising as it might sound, how often you work out can have a significant effect on your mental well-being. There is a strong connection between our mind and physical body; to the extent that taking care of one will positively affect the other.

When stress and anxiety affect the brain through series of nerves connected to it, the impact is felt in the rest of the body as well. And also, when your body is in great shape and feels good, your mind feels elated. Exercise produces chemicals in the brain called endorphins, which act as natural painkiller and enhance the ability to sleep. This reduces stress. Exercise is also vital in the maintenance of mental fitness, and very effective at revamping concentration and alertness, reducing fatigue and enhancing the overall cognitive functions in your body.

EXERCISE AS A REMEDY FOR STRESS AND ANXIETY DISORDER

The relevance of exercise extends beyond stress relief and improved mental well-being to encompass a significant enhancement in anxiety, mood and related disorders. As discussed in earlier chapters, stress and anxiety will occur regularly in the average human life. But in the case of stress and anxiety disorder, research proves it is the most common cause of psychiatric illnesses, and it affects over 30 million adults in the U.S. For the vast majority of individuals with depression and anxiety disorder, getting on medications or seeing a therapist is usually their go-to treatment. Whilst these options can be adequately helpful, there are a series of other factors that plays a vital role in dealing with anxiety disorder, and physical exercise is one of them.

Research shows that participating regularly in physical exercise will exhilarate and stabilize mood, improve sleep patterns and self-esteem, and reduce the overall levels of tension in the body. This research also shows that individuals who participate in frequent energetic exercise are 25 percent less liable to experience depression or anxiety disorder. A simple exercise relief like taking an aspirin for a headache or a brisk walk or hike can compensate for several hours of discomfort. One vigorous aerobic exercise can relieve symptoms for days, and periodic schedules will significantly decrease these symptoms in the long run.

Participating regularly in closely scheduled exercise will help reduce the symptoms of stress and anxiety disorder in the following ways:

- By distracting you from becoming increasingly worrisome by eradicating thoughts that trigger depression and anxiety.

- By secreting endorphins (which are responsible for causing feel-good feelings), endogenous cannabinoids (natural cannabis-like chemicals) and other brain chemicals that improve alertness and concentration and your overall sense of mental well-being.

The emotional and psychological benefits associated with brisk regular exercise and physical activities include:

- Engagement in more social relations; physical exercise, whether indoors or outdoors, creates a medium to meet and mingle with others in your city or town. A friendly smile here, a brief greeting there while you go about your exercise can help elevate your mood.

- Boosts self-confidence; achieving exercise goals and challenges, no matter how small, boosts your self-worth and self-confidence.

HOW MUCH EXERCISE IS REQUIRED?

Any exercise is better than no exercise at all. By engaging in a 30 to 45-minute daily exercise for three to five days a week, you'll experience a significant improvement in depression and stress levels, as well as in anxiety symptoms. Other physical activities lasting for as little as 5 to 15 minutes at a given time can make a difference. It is not mandatory that you do all your exercise and/or other physical activities at once. Change your perspective of how you think of exercise and improvise on ways to add and infuse small amounts of physical activities to your daily routines throughout your day. For instance, try taking the stairs instead of using the elevator, or fit in a short, daily walk by parking a little farther away from your workplace than you previously did. You can also consider biking to work if you do not live too far from your workplace. The required and adequate mental health benefits of exercise and physical activities will last only when you diligently stick to your routine over a long period of time.

GETTING STARTED AND STAYING MOTIVATED

Planning and adhering diligently to exercise routines or other physical activities can be challenging, but it is definitely doable. These routines and activities must be structured in such a way that you will be motivated to do more. Here are a few tips to guide you:

1. **What do you enjoy doing:** Examine yourself and figure out the type of exercise and/or physical activities you are most likely to do. Consider activities that will inspire you to do more. Think about what time and methods you would use to ensure you will most likely follow through on your decision. For instance, you can start your day with a jog or a brisk walk, go for a bike ride, play basketball with your friends on the weekend, etc. Doing exercise and physical activities that you enjoy will inspire you to do more and help you stick with it.

160

2. **Set reasonable and Achievable Goals:** The aim is not to exhaust yourself with long hours of physical activity or vigorous exercise that will leave you weak and helpless to carry out other daily responsibilities. In a logical manner, think about what you can and will be able to do; then, working gradually, continually improve upon your successes. This is far better than setting incoherent guidelines and targets you're unlikely to achieve; therefore, structure a workout plan that best suits your own needs and current abilities.

3. **Change your Perspective about Exercise and physical Activities:** Regard exercise and physical activities with the same esteem as your therapy sessions or medications. Consider them one of the many tools structured to help you get better and improve your overall mental well-being. The moment you think of exercise

or physical activity as a chore, and one you don't think you can live up to, you'll likely fail to reach your goals which may cause you to sink further into depression.

4. **Identify your Barriers:** Critically observe yourself and analyze what is stopping you from exercising or being physically active. Are you self-conscious? Then make adequate plans for a private exercise routine at home, or engage in physical activities during hours when you'll have less interaction with people. If exercising with a partner or having people around you while you work out is what inspires you and makes you stick to your goals better, then register with a local gym near you or find a workout partner in the form of a friend from work or a neighbor, or anyone who enjoys physical activities similar to the ones you do. If you don't have enough money in your budget to spend on exercise

gear, you can choose to do something that is cost-free, such as regularly walking or running. If you are motivated enough, you can find an alternative solution to whatever is stopping you from exercising or being physically active.

5. **Brace yourself for Setbacks and Obstacles:** There are days when you'll skip an exercise or a workout plan for a day or two, but that doesn't mean you can't maintain or follow through on an exercise routine, and it's not enough reason for you to quit. For every step you take in the right direction, give yourself credit, no matter how small. Always try as much as possible to get back on track the next day, and stick with it.

SUITABLE EXERCISE FOR MAXIMUM EFFECT

Any type of exercise and physical activity is useful, as long as it fits into your plan and you are available to do enough of it. Depending on your circumstances and how severe your situation is, recent federal guidelines recommend several minutes of moderate-intensity exercise and physical activity for adults experiencing stress and anxiety disorder.

For happiness-inducing aerobic exercise and physical activity to relieve stress and anxiety disorder and attain maximum mental well-being, engage diligently in the following exercises:

1. **Running or Jogging**

Over time, and for good reason, running or jogging has been one of the best exercises to promote sound health: it reduces food cravings, torches calories, and significantly lowers your risk for heart diseases. A mere five minute run or jog daily can help you live longer. It's one of the best go-to exercises when you're feeling down. It secretes endorphins, a bunch of cannabis-like, feel-good chemicals in your body responsible for giving euphoric feelings.

According to a study from the journal Comprehensive Psychiatry, the effects of running or jogging aren't just short-term. They cause long lasting changes in our feel-good neurotransmitters, serotonin and norepinephrine, both during and well after the exercise. Research shows that running or jogging is just as potent as psychotherapy in reducing the symptoms of stress and anxiety disorder. The repetitive motions of running or jogging have a meditative effect on the brain. And finally, a good run or jog can make it a lot easier for you to sleep at night, which enhances your overall mental health and well-being by lowering your stress levels, improving alertness, concentration and memory, thereby protecting you against fear and anxiety disorders.

2. **Hiking**

To maximize the full potentials and benefits of physical activity, consider hitting the trails and going for a hike. Apart from hiking being a mood-boosting cardiovascular activity, it involves being outside and spending an appreciable amount of time surrounded by nature. Evidence shows that being surrounded by plants and trees, most especially decaying trees, aids in reducing anxiety because of the chemicals emitted by these trees and plants to slow down their decaying process, which has been found to slow us down as well.

According to a study in 2009 from the Environmental Health and Preventive Medicine Journal, individuals who engage in a 20 to 30-minute walk in the woods (forest bath) experienced lower levels of stress hormones compared to those who took a walk for the same amount of time in the city. Walkers in the woods experienced enhanced memory function and felt less anxious. This research reinforces the notion that being adequately enwrapped by nature is a good way to improve mental health and overall well-being. Nature has its own calming effects.

3. **Yoga**

Generally, yoga is the go-to exercise for a vast majority of individuals aiming to attain a high level of relaxation. It focuses on slow, deep breaths and internal focus, which is advantageous to people dealing with stress and anxiety. According to experts, yoga's focus on deep breaths is significantly beneficial to your mental well-being because it's very difficult, if not nearly impossible to be anxious while breathing deeply. And, as such, individuals who engage in yoga classes experience significant reductions in stress, anxiety, anger, and other neurotic symptoms. You can try one of the many relaxing tricks called the 4-7-8 breathing technique, popularized by Andrew Weil, MD. By practicing yoga as an exercise, you'll experience its three main components: gentle stretching and core strengthening, breathing control exercises and meditation as a mind-body intervention.

4. **Dancing**

From salsa dancing, to enrolling in a zumba class or just grooving to some music on your iPod or in the comfort of your home, dancing provides its own form of relief enhancement from stress and anxiety. Studies show that enrolling and engaging in dance classes can reduce anxiety and stress as much as regular exercise and physical activities. Apart from being a form of physical activity, it is perceived by many as a form of personal expression, which can also help fortify the connection between the body and the mind. Enroll in a dance class today, and you'll experience an amazing change in your stress and anxiety levels.

5. **Tai Chi**

Practiced in China as a form of exercise as well as a martial art, Tai Chi is a form of exercise that blends

Chinese martial arts with meditative movements. It involves movement from a standing position through a series of postures likened to a choreographed dance. Its many sequences of postures are widely known as "forms", and it requires devoting a significant amount of time and concentration to fully master them.

According to research published in the International Journal of Behavioral Medicine, individuals who practice Tai Chi demonstrate high levels of improvement in areas of anxiety and general stress management. The workout involves physical balance, muscle relaxation, relaxed breathing, and mental concentration, all of which have being found to play a vital role in regulating stress and anxiety.

MEDITATION

For most individuals, the word meditation refers to sitting in a posture that allows for deep concentration or hanging out with some monks on the hills of Nepal or Tibet. While these are general ideas about meditation, the concept involves far more than the scenario described. Meditation is one of the best natural remedies for curing and managing the major psychological issues we have discussed in previous chapters. In discussing meditation, this section begins by identifying the origin of meditation, its development over the past centuries, practical guides to meditating in your home, and the mechanism by which meditation works in curing mood, anxiety disorders and chronic stress.

ORIGIN OF MEDITATION

The exact date of meditation's origin is unknown. There are evidences that suggest meditation was practiced as early as 5,000 to 3500 BC based on drawings on the walls of the Indus Valley as discovered by archeologists. The earliest images discovered show people sitting down in ways we can easily identify as meditation postures.

The earliest scriptural evidence of meditation can be found in those of Indian origin dating back to about 3,000 years ago. Clearly, no one knows when the act of meditation actually started; it may have been a happy accident. Earliest religions of the world have a lot of their followers practicing meditation, to include Buddhism, Taoism, and Christianity, etc. The only certainty in regards to meditation is that its most structured form can be related with what was common in Ancient India.

Initially, meditation was adopted as a means to get closer to the creator and seek enlightenment about his ways and commands. The Buddhist form of meditation developed to a level where it was believed that meditation was not a way to seek the face of the creator, but rather, it was a means of searching for the self-realization and inner peace every individual should desire.

In Japan, a monk named 'Dosho' was vital to the development of meditation as an art form as he gave directions in manuals called 'Zazen' on how meditation could be carried out while sitting. At this stage, the clear distinction between meditation and religion was already well pronounced, although certain religions still adopted meditation and perform it even now.

Meditation gained prominence in the Western World around the 20th century. It was at this point that medical researchers began to investigate the usefulness of meditation and learn more about the subject. During that time, it was not considered a tool for the healthcare system in solving psychological challenges.

However, Dr. Herbert Benson, one of the leading researchers of meditation, was a Harvard scholar who published several articles on the impact of meditation on improving the health of individuals. He discovered that many of the challenges we face today, including stress and anxiety disorders, can be managed by learning the basic techniques of meditation and fully adopting the practices.

TECHNIQUES OF MEDITATION

There are different types of meditation techniques adopted by individuals all over the world. The essence of this section is not to identify one particular technique that can remedy all problems, but to reveal various ones you can adopt. There is no 'best' or 'most effective technique' of mediation, and you can utilize anyone you are conversant with. The general types of meditation are focused primarily on attention and open monitoring meditation.

FOCUSED ATTENTION MEDITATION

Focused attention meditation encourages focusing on a particular object during meditation. The object being focused on could be your most treasured asset or loved one, your favorite place in the world, someone you are missing, etc. The object could even be a mantra, part of a body, visualization, etc. The idea of this technique is to make sure you continually focus on that particular object while blocking every other thought that may come into your mind. As you become an expert, things you worried about, i.e. financial troubles, divorce, etc., become forgotten at that particular point in time. It is believed that as long as you can train your mind to put all attention on one object, you can manage all those stressful situations you may have been facing. The idea is that once you become an expert at this, the troubles you face will not derail you to the extent of losing focus.

Many individuals find this form of meditation

easy to adopt, more than classic meditation, which can be considered harder due to the fact that you are focusing on nothing. Our mind is very powerful, and as such, it could wander off when blank. As a beginner in the art of meditation, you can start with focus meditation and later adopt the classical method for a change. The steps to practice focused mediation are discussed below.

1.) **Picking out the object to focus on**

This is naturally the first stage of focused meditation. You need to make your choice as regards to what you want to focus on. You are advised to choose anything that puts you at peace in this stage of the process.

2.) **Adopt a very comfortable position for you**

Meditation can only be effective when you relax your body. You should take deep breaths in and out to ensure the proper circulation of oxygen and carbon dioxide around your body. Also, you are advised not to pick a position that will encourage you to sleep. Instead, pick one that ensures you are truly relaxed.

3.) **Embrace your chosen target**

The idea of choosing and focusing on a target is to ensure that you embrace it and that you are at peace with that target. Every component of that target should be formed in your mind in such a way that you have the picture of it all in your mind at the time. Capturing that picture should be effortless as the goal is to be at one with the object.

4.) **Manage that inner voice**

It is normal that your inner voice would want you to wander off to another place. It could be the troubles you have faced over the last few months, or how those whom you trusted have let you down. In other circumstances, your inner voice may try to lead you to the challenges and quarrels you had that morning with your colleague at work or with your neighbor. Whatever it may be, this period is not the time for it. Controlling your inner voice gives you the much needed skills to learn how to block out distractions.

5.) **Don't be afraid of failing**

Hardly anyone gets a new experience right the first time. Do not give up because you feel the first time you tried this out was tough, or it didn't work. You must have heard the sentence 'you lose 100 percent of the shots you do not take.' This aptly describes what happens if you do not get meditation right the first time. All the experts on the subject, including monks, took years to master the art of meditation. Nothing is a day's job; you have to be ready to try again and again. Of course, you should not have the mindset of failure, but when set-backs happen, be eager to try again.

OPEN MONITORING MEDITATION

With focused meditation, you were encouraged to direct your mind at one particular object that serves as your guide in the process of meditation while eliminating all other thoughts, visuals, or even sensations that may come to your mind. Open monitoring meditation is different from focused meditation in terms of the process and mechanism of operation. Here, you are encouraged to allow every thought, idea, smell or object visualized into your mind. This technique of meditation teaches that everything you think of is a part of the constant energy following and radiating through your mind. As such, they are part and parcel of you as an individual.

Open monitoring meditation, thus, teaches that all those things be allowed into your heart, and you evaluate them as they come. As such, your mind is a funnel which is open to every thought that may come through. A key quote to be remembered in regards to open monitoring meditation is that nothing is to be avoided, and everything is to be left as it is. This basically means you should take in all i.e. every pain, all the guilt, anger and disappointment, ever expression, and all that you may be feeling.

This also implies that you are only observing what is happening within you without any form of affiliation to any one thought or addiction. You are merely monitoring what is happening without guiding your thoughts on where they should lead to, or not. You are expected to be still while observing the flow of thought without being a judge of any. The steps to be adopted in practicing open meditation are as follows:

1.) **Get a calm place**

You are in the best position to determine the best place in your environment where you can meditate without any form of distraction. You could decide to pick a period when everyone is asleep or has gone to work or school. In ensuring the effectiveness of this form of mediation, you have to make sure that whatever time or place you pick is one that gives you free reign to focus your undivided attention.

2.) **Ensure you are comfortable**

No matter the form of meditation you adopt, you'll require a high level of comfort because the only way meditation can work is if you are relaxed. You can decide to adopt a sitting position on the floor, the lotus position, or you can even sit down on a chair or lie down on a mat on the floor. Whatever position you pick, you must be careful not to fall asleep. Falling asleep while meditating defeats the whole purpose.

3.) **Start observing**

The room is silent (from step 1) and therefore you should be able to hear your heartbeat. In your present position, you should feel all your organs and sensory functions. The thoughts should start flowing through like a form of energy. You should be at ease, similar to a situation where you are watching a movie you have no interest in. Remember that your only duty is to observe without passing any judgment. You are not the referee, and at this time, just know that you can't afford to get emotional. Do not try to block any thought that may come into your mind. It could even be a violent thought that you conceived at some point but never acted upon. Let it all flow. Block none of it.

4.) **Switch your focus to the external**

It helps better when you can easily alter your focus to the outside of your being. It could be a song you heard at some point in the past, or objects in the room. You can smell those sensations in your room, or whatever comes to you.

5.) **Be ready to retry**

If you feel you did not get it right the first time, you could be judging those thoughts and emotions you experienced, or perhaps that meditation attempt was an indication that you were distracted and you have to try it again. You may not find the inner peace you desire the first time you try, but that is no excuse to jump ship. My honest opinion here is that you try and retry again until you perfect it.

OTHER TYPES OF MEDITATION FOR STRESS AND ANXIETY

The types of meditation discussed in the previous sections are the two popular types in literature. This section focuses on different meditation techniques you can adopt in unique cases of stress, mood and anxiety disorder. We have evidence of their resounding success in carefully managing the psychological rigors anyone may be facing. If practiced regularly, you can be assured there would be a difference in your health within a month or two. As such, these meditation practices are not to be abandoned. Even after noticing an improvement in your health, you still have to continue practicing. Meditation, as we advise here, should be a notable part of your life. You can view meditation as a form of food that you can eat daily.

The types of meditation to alleviate stress, depression and anxiety disorder are:

1.) **Loving and Kindness meditation**

This type of meditation, also known as 'Metta bhavana', helps to develop love and compassion. Its origin can be traced to the Buddhist tradition, but has been adopted in the present 21st century by people seeking to control stress. Individuals who practice it have reported an increase in their capacity to easily forgive others while reducing the internal tensions they face. For a therapy that requires less than an hour of your time daily, it is certainly worthwhile to try it out. The technique adopted is to ensure you deliberately direct that loving energy at yourself and those around you.

Loving-kindness, as identified here, refers to inclusive, unconditional love which does not rely on whether the individuals you are directing it at deserve it or not. Here, there are no criteria for expressing love to anyone. It is often easy to claim we love someone who has been nice or good to us in the past. Pure love is not about reciprocating the good deeds we have benefitted from in the past, but loving someone no matter the circumstances surrounding them. Imagine the type of love a parent would have for his or her child. What has the child done to receive that enormous amount of love from the parent? Nothing. This type of meditation focuses on having that type of love for everyone regardless of how we think we might have been treated.

To carry this out, you need to love yourself. You cannot blame yourself for everything that has happened to you in the past. You need to let go of every resentment or ill-feeling you may have attached to yourself. Some may think 'if only I was beautiful enough,' 'if only I was there at the time,' 'if only I had listened to him.' Thinking of 'ifs' only lead to continuous breeding of regrets every day of our lives, which is not a good way to live.

After making peace with every circumstance you may have found yourself in, you need to apply that scenario to everyone around you. As humans, it is natural that we make mistakes in our dealings with other people. We may even make decisions that affect others deliberately, but despite that, there is some goodness in all our hearts. A loving-kindness meditation ensures that we are able to see that goodness while promoting our own stress-free life. The decision to that rests solely in our hands.

The steps to take in practicing the loving kindness meditation are

i.   Create time for yourself where you will have the opportunity to be alone. As discussed in earlier techniques, you need spaces with no distraction whatsoever if you want to be successful at this.

ii.   Create a setting in your mind where you are blessed with inner peace and emotional satisfaction. You can psych yourself into believing you have perfect, unblemished love for yourself. Try to direct your attention to that inner peace while activating your respiratory organs.

iii.   You should have your catch phrases with reassuring words you declare to yourself. Here, the power of positive thinking is channeled into making sure you believe everything you are saying. Sayings like 'I am a happy man,' 'I am in love with myself.'

MINDFULNESS

Mindfulness is an exceptionally basic type of meditation that was minimally known in the West until recently. A regular meditation comprises of concentrating your complete deliberation on your breath as it streams all through your body. Concentrating on every breath this way enables you to observe your thoughts as they emerge in your mind and, little by little, to relinquish battling with them. You come to understand that thoughts go back and forth voluntarily; that you are not your thoughts. You can observe as they appear in your mind, apparently from thin air, and observe again as they vanish, similar to a bubble blasting. You begin to significantly understand that thoughts and emotions (including negative ones) are transient. They come and they go, and at last, you have a decision whether you will follow up on them or not.

Mindfulness is about observation without criticism, and about showing compassion to yourself.

Whenever sadness or stress floats overhead, instead of thinking about it all literally, you figure out how to regard them as though they were dark mists in the sky, and to watch them with benevolent interest as they float past. Basically, mindfulness enables you to trap negative thought patterns before they tip you into a descending spiral. It starts by placing you in a position whereby you are responsible for your life.

After some time, mindfulness achieves long term changes in stress and your level of bliss and well-being. Research has demonstrated that mindfulness prevents depression, as well as decisively influences the brain patterns of everyday anxiety, stress, depression and irritability with the goal that when they emerge, they break down more effortlessly. Different studies have demonstrated that consistent meditators see their therapists less frequently and spend less time in the hospital. Memory enhancement, increments in creativity and response time turn out to be faster.

In spite of these demonstrated advantages, nonetheless, many individuals are still a little watchful when they hear the word "meditation". So before we continue, it may be useful to dissipate a few myths:

- Meditation isn't a religion. Mindfulness is just a strategy for mental training. Many individuals who practice meditation are themselves religious; however, on the other hand, numerous skeptics and rationalists are sharp meditators, as well.

- You don't need to sit with folded legs on the floor (like the photos you may have found in magazines or on TV); however you can, if by any chance you need to. A great many people who go to meditation classes sit on chairs to think, however you can likewise work on conveying mindful awareness to whatever you are doing, on public buses, trains or while strolling to work. You can ponder pretty much anywhere you find yourself.

- Mindfulness does not take a lot of time, although some tolerance and determination are required. Many individuals soon find that meditation frees them from the pressures of time, so they have a greater amount of it to spend on different things.

- Meditation isn't entangled, nor is it about "achievement" or "failure". Notwithstanding, when meditation feels difficult, you'll have picked up something profitable about the workings of the mind, and in this way, have profited mentally.

- It will not stifle your psyche or keep you from striving towards important career or lifestyle objectives; nor will it deceive you into erroneously embracing a Pollyanna attitude toward life. Meditation isn't tied in with tolerating the unsuitable. It is tied in with seeing the world with more noteworthy lucidity so you can make more astute and more considered decisions to change those things which should be changed. Meditation develops a profound and empathetic awareness that enables you to evaluate your objectives and locate the ideal path towards understanding your most profound esteems.

Mindfulness likewise includes acceptance, implying that we focus on our thoughts and emotions without passing judgment on them, for example, that there's a "right" or "wrong" approach to think or feel in a given minute. When we practice mindfulness, our thoughts tune into what we're detecting right now as opposed to reiterating the past or envisioning what is yet to come.

In spite of the fact that it has its underlying foundations in Buddhist meditation, a common routine with regards to mindfulness has entered the American standard, of late, to some degree, through the work of Jon Kabat-Zinn and his Mindfulness-Based Stress

Reduction (MBSR) program, which he propelled at the University of Massachusetts Medical School in 1979. Since that time, a large number of studies have reported the physical and psychological wellness advantages of mindfulness in general, and MBSR specifically, inspiring endless projects to adjust the MBSR model for schools, prisons, veterans' centers, etc.

MINDFULNESS AND MENTAL WELL-BEING

By becoming more mindful of the present moment and keeping up a moment-by-moment awareness of your thoughts, bodily sensations and feelings, mindfulness can enable you to increasingly appreciate your general surroundings and comprehend yourself better. When you turn out to be more mindful of the present moment, you start to encounter, once again, things that you have been underestimating.

By becoming more mindful of the surge of thoughts and feeling that you encounter, you'll have the capacity to perceive how you've turned out to be ensnared in that stream of thought in ways that are not useful. This enables you to stand back from your thoughts and begin to see their patterns. Steadily, you'll have the capacity to coach yourself to see when your thoughts are assuming control, and you'll come to understand that thoughts are essentially "mental events" that you don't have control over.

It's normal to have issues that are hard to give up, and mindfulness can assist you in managing them efficiently. You may ask: "Is attempting to unravel this by brooding about it helpful, or am I simply becoming involved with my thoughts?" In addition, awareness of this kind encourages you to see symptoms of stress and anxiety at an early stage and enables you to manage them better. Mindfulness is recommended by the National Institute for Health and Care Excellence (NICE) as an approach to prevent depression in individuals who have had at least three prior episodes of depression.

BASIC MINDFULNESS EXERCISES

A lot of us don't have five minutes to take a seat and unwind, not to mention 30 minutes or more for a meditation session. In any case, for the sake of your health, it is imperative to take a couple of minutes every day to develop mental openness and accomplish a positive mind-body balance.

So if, by any chance, you are a bustling honey bee like me, you can utilize these basic mindfulness activities to discharge your mind and locate some genuinely necessary calm in the midst of the franticness of your boisterous day.

These activities require next to no exertion and should be possible basically whenever and wherever you find yourself:

MINDFUL BREATHING

This activity should be possible standing up or taking a seat, and basically whenever and wherever you find yourself. In the event that you can take a seat in the meditation (lotus) position, that is great, but if not, do not stress. In any case, you should simply be still and concentrate on your breath for only one moment.

- Begin by breathing in and out gradually. One breath cycle should keep going for roughly six seconds.

- Take a deep breath in through your nose and out through your mouth, giving your breath a chance to stream easily all through your body.

- Relinquish your thoughts; relinquish things you need to do later today, or pending undertakings that need your attention. Basically let thoughts rise and fall voluntarily and be at one with your breath.

- Deliberately observe your breath, concentrating your sense of awareness on its pathway as it enters your body and fills you with life.

- At that point, observe your awareness as it works its way up and out of your mouth and its vitality scatters into the world.

In the event that you're someone who thought they'd never have the capacity to meditate, prepare to have your mind blown. As of now, you are nearly there!

And if by any chance you enjoyed one moment of this mind-calming exercise, what reason could you have for not attempting a few more?

MINDFUL OBSERVATION

This exercise is basic, yet amazingly intense in light of the fact that it causes you to see and acknowledge apparently direct components of your environment in a more significant manner. The exercise is intended to impress upon you the beauty of the natural environment, something that is not entirely obvious when you are swerving around in cars or jumping on and off trains while in transit to work.

- Pick a natural object from within your immediate vicinity and concentrate on watching it for a moment. This could be a flower blossom or a bug, a mist, or the moon.

- Try not to do anything aside from seeing the thing you are taking a gander at. Just unwind into looking at the object for whatever length of time that your focus permits.

- Take a gander at this object as though you are seeing it out of the blue.

- Visually investigate each part of its development, and permit yourself to be devoured by its essence.

- Permit yourself to interact with its vitality and its motivation within the ordinary world.

MINDFUL AWARENESS

This exercise is intended to develop an increased awareness and appreciation of basic daily tasks and the outcomes they accomplish. Consider something that happens each day more than once; something you underestimate, such as opening a door, for instance. At the exact instant you touch the doorknob to open the door, stop for a minute and be aware of where you are, the way in which you feel at that time and where the door will lead you.

Also, the minute you open your PC to begin work, pause for a minute to value the hands that empower this procedure and the brain that encourages your comprehension of how to utilize the PC. These 'touch point' prompts don't necessarily have to be physical ones. For instance: Each time you think a negative idea, you may pause for a minute to name the idea as unhelpful and discharge the antagonism.

Or, then again, maybe each time you smell food, you pause for a minute to stop and acknowledge that you are so fortunate to have great nourishment to eat and share with your friends and families.

Pick a touch point that impacts you today and, rather than experiencing your day-to-day movements on autopilot, take infrequent minutes to stop and develop deliberate consciousness of what you are doing and the endowments these activities convey to your life.

MINDFUL LISTENING

This exercise is intended to open your ears to sound in a non-judgmental manner, and to coach your psyche (mind) to be less influenced by the impact of past encounters and assumptions. Such an extensive amount of what we "feel" is affected by past understanding. For instance, we may hate a melody since it reminds us of a breakup or another time in life when things felt negative. So the possibility of this activity is to hear some music from an impartial point of view, with a present mindfulness that is unhindered by previously established inclinations.

Select a bit of music you have never heard. You may have something from your own collection that you have never tuned in to, or you may tune the radio dial until the point when something catches your attention.

- Close your eyes and put on your earphones.

- Do whatever it takes not to get drawn into judging the music by its classification (genre), title, or the name of the artist. Rather, disregard any marks and impartially permit yourself to lose all sense of direction in the trip of sound for the span of the tune.

- Permit yourself to explore each part of the track. Regardless of the possibility that the music isn't to your taste initially, let go of your aversion and give your awareness full authorization to move inside the track and along with the sound waves.

- Explore the melody by tuning in to the elements of each instrument. Isolate each sound in your mind and examine each one by one.

- Focus on the vocals: the sound of the voice, its range and tones. If by any chance there is more than one voice, isolate them out as you did in the previous stage.

The aim is to listen closely and carefully, to end up noticeably and completely interwoven with the piece without any previously established inclination or judgment of the artist, lyrics, genre or instrumentation. Try not to think. Simply hear.

MINDFUL IMMERSION

The expectation of this exercise is to develop happiness in the moment and escape the determined endeavors we get ourselves entangled in on a daily basis. As opposed to restlessly needing to complete an ordinary routine undertaking, keeping in mind the end goal you'll get with accomplishing something different, take that regular routine and completely encounter it more than you ever have. For instance; in the event that you are cleaning your home, focus on everything about the movement.

As opposed to regarding this as a standard task, make it a completely new affair by seeing each part of your activity: Feel and tune into the movement when clearing the floor, sense the muscles you utilize when scouring the dishes, build up a more effective method for cleaning the windows. The aim is to get imaginative and find new encounters inside a natural routine assignment.

GUSTAVO KINRYS, M.D.

Rather than working through and continually considering completing the assignment, wind up noticeably mindful of each progression and completely submerge yourself in the advance. Take the action past a routine by adjusting yourself to it physically, rationally and spiritually.

Who knows, you may even appreciate cleaning after such an experience!

MINDFUL APPRECIATION

With mindful appreciation, you are simply asked to observe five things in your day that typically go unacknowledged. These things can be objects or individuals; it's entirely up to you. You can make use of a scratch pad to confirm these five things before the day is over. The purpose of this activity is to just express appreciation, and value the apparent immaterial things in life, the things that help our reality, yet seldom get noticed in the midst of our desire for more and better things.

For instance, electric power energizes your PC, the postman conveys your mail, your garments give you warmth, your nose gives you a chance to smell the flower blossoms in the park, and your ears let you hear the feathered creatures in the trees by the bus terminal, yet.....

Do you know how these things/forms came to exist, or how they truly work? Have you, at any point, appropriately recognized how these things are advantageous to your life and the lives of others? Have you at any point considered what life might look like without these things? Have you at any point halted to see their better, more unpredictable subtle elements? Have you at any point sat down and contemplated the connections between these things and how, together, they assume an interconnected part in the workings of the earth?

When you have recognized your five things, make it your obligation to discover all that you can about their creation and find a reason to genuinely value the part they play in bettering your life.

TRANSCRANIAL MAGNETIC STIMULATION (TMS)

Transcranial Magnetic Stimulation (TMS) treatment has been determined as safe option for depression and anxiety disorders. This non-invasive neuro-modulation treatment has been researched to treat a few mental and neurological disorders like depression, bipolar disorder, post-traumatic stress disorder (PTSD), obsessive-compulsive disorder (OCD), chronic pain and Alzheimer`s disease, among others.

Its mechanism of action includes the discharge of magnetic pulses with a coil situated over a pre-characterized region of the scalp. These magnetic pulses go through the skull toward the objective brain region. The stimulation with TMS aims to reach hypoactive and hyperactive areas of the brain to adjust brain connectivity networks. Repetitive TMS (rTMS) has been affirmed by numerous regulatory agencies for the treatment of treatment-resistant Depression (TRD). Studies have demonstrated that TMS is helpful in the treatment of TRD through changes in neuronal movement in a few areas of the brain identified with mood regulation and control, for example, the prefrontal cortex. Be that as it may, the treatment with rTMS for other treatment-resistant psychiatric disorders is, at the time of this publication, considered to be experimental.

The statistics of studies assessing the treatment of other psychiatric and neurological disorders with TMS is constantly growing. However, some researchers are still investigating the treatment of resistant anxiety and traumatic disorders with TMS. Symptoms of anxiety, fear and stress may result in dysfunctional conditions that can be chronic and prompt PTSD or anxiety disorders. PTSD is unequivocally co-morbid to other psychiatric disorders with lifetime co-morbidity rates that range from 62 to 92 percent. Besides, there is proof that Panic disorder (PD), generalized anxiety disorder (GAD), and PTSD may have a typical hereditary inclination.

In this manner, TMS might be a possibility for treatment-resistant diseases and additionally for people that are delicate to psychotropic medication side effects. Additionally, some unfavorable events that have been related to the utilization of antidepressants, which are the primary line treatment for anxiety disorders and PTSD, such as dry mouth, weight gain, gastrointestinal symptoms, sexual dysfunction, and sedation, might be averted with TMS. Then again, TMS can likewise cause side effects. The most widely recognized side effect is a headache, revealed by half of the patients treated with TMS. For the most part, the headaches are gentle and diminish before the end of the treatment. Over-the-counter pain medications can also be utilized to treat these issues.

VIRTUAL REALITY TREATMENT

Virtual Reality (VR) Treatment offers an innovative human-computer interaction method of therapy for individuals experiencing anxiety disorder due to different phobias, such as fear of flying, heights, thunderstorms, elevators and public speaking. A preliminary diagnostic interview is first conducted to certify that the treatment is apt for the presenting problem. The individual is then placed in a computer-generated 3D virtual world and guided through the selected environment. Various computer graphic displays and input technologies are integrated to provide you with the required sense of immersion in the virtual environment. The therapist then guides you through the environment and also interacts with you throughout the entire process. Studies have shown that 6 to 12 sessions are usually required to achieve maximum benefit.

Recently, Virtual Reality has been experiencing massive popularity among tech-enthusiasts due to the amazing 3D immersive gaming and theater experience it provides. With its use expanding far beyond mere entertainment, Virtual Reality is becoming more readily available. The immersive nature of Virtual Reality has proven to be a valuable technology for designing equipment for the treatment of certain psychological disorders. Anxiety, phobias, stress and post-traumatic stress disorder are distinctively managed and treated using Virtual Reality exposure therapy (VRET).

VR TREATMENT FOR PHOBIAS AND ANXIETY

With the increasing number of people in the US experiencing anxiety and phobias, it has become necessary and exceedingly appealing to make use of decentralized healthcare through telemedicine. Virtual Reality treatment provides people experiencing phobias and anxiety with self-guided exposure therapy that has the potential to make a real difference in the patient's psychological well-being. The VR exposure therapy combines and exposes the patient to the most suitable cognitive behavioral therapy, which allows such individuals to go through their fears in a genuine and realistically simulated environment without actually leaving the luxury, comfort, and safety of the therapist's office.

Virtual Reality has also recently being designed and integrated with game-like psychological treatment tools to help individuals experience phobias and anxiety without the involvement of a therapist. Although there seems to be no substitute for professional involvement in the treatment of phobias and anxiety, a majority of those who suffer phobias never seek medical or professional help, which might make this therapeutic game an ideal psychological treatment device for self-help!

VR TREATMENT FOR STRESS RELIEF

Virtual Reality treatment is also very much helpful to those suffering from stress. The treatment is offered through immersive meditative experiences. A typical example of such a simulation is DEEP: a meditative and psychoactive Virtual reality simulation that is totally controlled by the user's breathing. The game-like VR simulation instantaneously transports you to a placid environment where the basic breathing principles of yoga are employed to help you relax and stay calm. The potential health benefits of a VR exposure treatment are remarkable, being able to immerse yourself in a meditative experience, irrespective of your location is indeed a unique type of therapy. Relaxing on the beach doesn't have to occur only when you're on annual vacation. It's just a "VR goggle away."

VR TREATMENT FOR POST-TRAUMATIC STRESS DISORDER (PTSD)

For decades, Virtual Reality exposure therapy (VRET) has been administered to individuals with post-traumatic stress disorder (PTSD). Conventionally, VR treatment was extremely expensive as the technology was sparse and costly. However, recent technological innovations have made Virtual Reality devices as readily accessible as smartphones. Therapists are now better equipped to use VR treatment to deliver concise and specialized exposure therapies to accident victims, war veterans, and other individuals suffering from PTSD.

With the recent popularity and availability of Virtual Reality technology, therapists can safely expose their patients to PTSD triggers such as loud noises and stressful situations or conditions in a bid to ultimately reduce their effect on the patient. Recent research has shown that Virtual Reality exposure therapy was similarly as effective and beneficial as drug therapy, but without any of the adverse side effects.

The benefits of Virtual Reality Treatment over traditional exposure therapy include:

- **Improved Safety and Control:** Virtual Reality Treatment basically involves exposure to a virtual environment containing the feared stimulus as an alternative to taking the patient to the real environment or having the patient visualize the stimulus, which is usually unpredictable or not effective enough. In VR Treatment, there are more controls over the virtual environment to ensure adequate and effective exposure to the programmed situations.

- **Comfortable Schedules and Effective Treatment:** The simulations of VR environments have been carefully designed to support exposure therapy for phobias and anxiety related disorders. While standard exposure therapy is more expensive due to the fact that it typically requires leaving the therapist's office and therefore resulting in extended sessions, virtual reality treatment can achieve the same exposure within the standard stipulated therapy hour and also inside the confines of the therapist's office. This brings about flexible and multiple scheduled sessions as many times as is possible or feasible.

- **Improved Patient Confidentiality:** VR treatment is conducted within the confines of the therapist's office to reduce the risk of running into friends or being in public when you encounter difficult conditions, or the exposure is more than you can bear.

- **Unlimited Recurrence of Feared Stimulus:** While standard exposure therapy is restricted to real life limitations, such as a single take-off and landing of an airplane, the VR treatment tolerates decisive control over stimuli in order to achieve the perfect exposure. Virtual reality treatment gives room for repetitive manipulation of the stimuli to best suit your conditions. For instance, repetitive taking-off and landing of a virtual airplane.

Over time, VR treatment has been certified by many studies to possess a prevailing real life impact. It has a great track record of successfully treating both adults and children with anxiety disorder, social anxiety, panic disorder, obsessive compulsive disorder (OCD), post-traumatic stress disorder (PTSD), and all forms of phobias. Additionally, it has proven effective as a treatment for children experiencing sleep fears and school phobia.

Virtual reality has moved beyond the gaming or immersive 3D theater experience. Now, it has the capacity to do so much more. The possibility of instantaneous virtual transportation to placid environments can make a significant difference in the lives of individuals experiencing phobia, anxiety and stress. Conceivably, VR treatment might even be more remarkable at treating survivors of traumatic events. However, the treatment is incapable of completely taking over the field of therapy. It is more of a complementary treatment for individuals whenever the need arises.

Table 3: Summary of Non-Pharmacological Treatments

Cognitive behavioral therapy (CBT)	Exercise	Meditation	Mindfulness	Transcranial Magnetic Stimulation (TMS)	Virtual Reality Treatment
Relaxation: Autogenic Training Breathing Dynamic muscle relaxation Meditation	Running or Jogging Hiking Yoga Dancing Tai Chi	Focused Attention Meditation Open Monitoring Meditation Loving and Kindness meditation	Mindful Breathing Mindful Observation Mindful Awareness Mindful Listening Mindful Immersion Mindful Appreciation	The stimulation with TMS expects to adjust hypoactive and hyperactive areas of the brain to adjust brain connectivity networks.	An innovative human-computer interaction method of therapy for individuals experiencing anxiety disorder due to different phobias, such as, fear of flying, heights, thunderstorms, elevators and public speaking.

REFERENCES

Abdou, A. M., Higashiguchi, S., Horie, K., Kim, M., Hatta, H., and Yokogoshi, H. (2006). Relaxation and immunity enhancement effects of γ-aminobutyric acid (GABA) administration in humans. Biofactors 26, 201–208. doi: 10.1002/biof.5520260305.

American Psychiatric Association, Diagnostic and Statistical Manual of Mental Disorders, American Psychiatric Association, Arlington, Va, USA, 4th edition, 2000.

Baek JH, Nierenberg AA, Kinrys G. Clinical applications of herbal medicines for anxiety and insomnia; targeting patients with bipolar disorder. Aust N Z J Psychiatry. 2014 Aug;48(8):705-15.

B. Bandelow, U. Seidler-Brandler, A. Becker, D. Wedekind, and E. Ruther, "Meta-analysis of randomized controlled comparisons of psychopharmacological and psychological treatments for anxiety disorders," World Journal of Biological Psychiatry, vol. 8, no. 3, pp. 175–187, 2007.

Garrett KM, Basmadjian G, Khan IA, Schaneberg BT, Seale TW: Extracts of kava (Piper methysticum) induce acute anxiolytic-like behavioral changes in mice. Psychopharmacology (Berl) 2003, 170:33-41.

J. Alonso, M. C. Angermeyer, S. Bernert et al., "Prevalence of mental disorders in Europe: results from the European Study of the Epidemiology of Mental Disorders (ESEMeD) project," ActaPsychiatricaScandinavica, Supplement, vol.420, no.420, pp. 21–27, 2004.

Kanehira, T., Yoshiko, N., Nakamura, K., Horie, K., Horie, N., Furugori, K., et al. (2011). Relieving occupational fatigue by consumption of a beverage containing γ-aminobutyricacid.J.Nutr.Sci.Vitaminol.57,9–15. doi:10.3177/ jnsv.57.9.

REFERENCES

Kinrys G, Coleman E, Rothstein E. Natural remedies for anxiety disorders: potential use and clinical applications. Depress Anxiety. 2009;26(3):259-65.

Lader M, Tylee A, Donoghue J: Withdrawing benzodiazepines in primary care. CNS Drugs 2009, 23:19-34.

Linde K, Ramirez G, Mulrow CD, Pauls A, Weidenhammer W, Melchart D: St John's wort for depression - an overview and meta-analysis of randomised clinical trials. BMJ 1996, 313.

Logan, A. C., and Katzman, M. (2005). Major depressive disorder: probiotics may be an adjuvant therapy. Med. Hypotheses 64, 533–538. doi: 10.1016/j.mehy.2004.08.019.

R. C. Kessler, T. C. Wai, O. Demler, and E. E. Walters, "Prevalence, Severity, and Comorbidityof12-monthDSM-IV disorders in the National Comorbidity Survey Replication," Archives of General Psychiatry, vol. 62, no. 6, pp. 617–627, 2005.

Watkins LL, K MC, J RD: Effect of kava extract on vagal cardiac control in generalized anxiety disorder: preliminary findings. Journal of psychopharmacology (Oxford, England) 2001, 15:283-286.

Made in the USA
Middletown, DE
07 December 2022